From Arundel to Z

A Cricket Followers' Guide to British and International Cricket Grounds

By Robin Osmond, Peter David Lush and Dave Farrar

County Cricket at Arundel (RO)

LONDON LEAGUE PUBLICATIONS Ltd.

From Arundel to Zimbabwe

A Cricket Followers' Guide to British and International Cricket Grounds

First published in Great Britain in April 1997 by:

London League Publications Ltd.
P.O. Box 10441
London E14 0SB

ISBN: 0-9526064-6-1

Cover design by: Stephen McCarthy Graphic Design
23, Carol Street, London NW1 0HT

Printed and bound by: Redwood Books, Trowbridge, Wiltshire.

About the Authors

Robin Osmond:

Is a former Director of Social Services and Social Services Consultant; he is a devoted Middlesex and Arsenal supporter, and has much enjoyed the numerous entertainments of West Country Village and County Cricket over the last eight years. He is a Member of the MCC, Gloucestershire and Glamorgan; very occasional left arm slow bowler (with chinaman) and cricket writer, he is currently a full time photography student and traveller to faraway places.

He feels that the importance of cricket administration generally and cricket grounds in particular have been undelvalued and hopes that this Guide will encourage cricket followers to explore the endless opportunities for watching cricket and that the authorities will respond positively to an informed and discriminating audience in the future.

Peter David Lush:

Is not a former TCCB official and England tour manager! (And is making rare use of his middle name to avoid unnecessary confusion). A Londoner, played for King Alfred School first XI - which was very short of players. Retired from playing Cricket at 16 after seeing Mike and Steve Gatting play at Brondesbury CC (in their younger days), and realising how far he was from reaching a reasonable standard. Made a comeback in his mid 30s to play for Malvern CC in east London, once taking five wickets, and played against future Middlesex star Paul Weekes, before finally retiring from active Cricket in 1989.

A Middlesex supporter, his main sporting interests apart from Cricket are Football (West Ham United) and Rugby League (London Broncos). Has co-written two Rugby League books with Dave Farrar, and is currently working on a third. When not researching sports books, and taking photos of sports grounds, he works as a freelance housing and personnel consultant.

Dave Farrar:

Born Salford, Lancashire. Now lives in Poplar, East London. Has been following Lancashire for nearly 30 years off and on and hopes to see them win the Championship before he retires. Has co-written three Rugby League books, writes and draws cartoons in his spare time. Works in Local Government Administration. Tail-end Charlie and exotic off-spin bowler during brief cricket career. Main sporting interest apart from Cricket is Rugby League (London Broncos).

Preface

Besides the great Test Match grounds relatively little has been written about the County cricket grounds which provide particular and essential local cricketing pleasures. There are countless memories of outstanding individual batting and bowling performances and epic Championship or Cup matches, apart from the nostalgic charms of ancient Kentish grounds or the delectable teas in the Ladies Pavilion at New Road, relatively little is known to the wider public about the grounds themselves.

The main objective of this book is to bring together basic information about all the grounds on which First Class cricket will be played during the 1997 season, including Scotland and Ireland, together with details of Minor Counties venues, and the major international Test Match grounds.

There are details of membership, ticket availability, general ground provision, travel directions and parking, catering facilities, access and facilities for people with disabilities and sketch maps of the grounds. The authors visited every English County ground during 1996 and we include pen portraits and photographs which we hope will convey some of the delights and varied pleasures of a day at the cricket in different settings.

County Cricket will be played at 52 different venues in the 1997 season, ranging from the imposing grandeur of Test arenas at their best on big occasions, to festival time at Bath and Cheltenham and the magical club grounds at Abergavenney and The Saffrons.

Readers will discover that cricket grounds bear little resemblance to each other in their layout, accommodation and facilities; they are unique in their history and development and until very recently were constrained by limited resources. But they are essentially members' clubs and have developed for the principal benefit of their traditional main sources of income, until corporate interests and entertainment provided new and even more seductive demands for attention.

For the general public and casual spectator, with notable exceptions, this can still mean hard seats and draughty stands; limited fast food and tasteless sandwiches; ancient loos; and inadequate facilities for people with disabilities. Much more needs to be done in cricket grounds for the potential audience for cricket watching besides the captive audience of club members and business entertainment.

Apart from the partisan rivalry of the Cup competitions when coachloads will descend on their opponent's ground, there is a relatively small nucleus of regular travellers and every reason for the County authorities to encourage and welcome the idea of visitors from other areas. Part of the thinking behind this book is to invite County Committees to consider more flexible admission practices and improvements in facilities and services for the general or more casual spectators. Surrey will be pioneering floodlight cricket in 1997; rather than sticking to a 6.30 pm close, varying the hours of play could mean a full evening session in high summer and prove very attractive to working cricket followers and club cricketers who play at weekends.

There are obviously increasing opportunities for watching cricket all the year round in the exciting surroundings of the Caribbean, Australasia and other countries. We believe that potential spectators should know in advance what is available so that they can ensure their requirements are met, and not be disappointed when they arrive at the Ground. We hope that the Guide will also assist people visiting international cricket venues both making their own way and on organised tours.

If the Guide is successful, it will be updated and become a regular event; in the meanwhile we hope that all cricket followers will enjoy their cricket and go out and visit some different grounds in 1997.

Robin Osmond
March 1997

Lara breaks the 365 record - the decisive moment. Antigua April 1994 (RO)

How to use this book

Road travel: We recommend using a standard road map with this book. The sketch maps are not drawn to scale, and only cover areas close to the grounds.

Facilities: All British first class grounds have tea, coffee, snacks and fast food available, and have toilets for people with disabilities, except where specified. For grounds used for festival weeks which are not primarily first class venues, the match day facilities outlined are usually only available at first class matches. We received information about admission of guide dogs and other facilities for the visually impaired close to our deadline. We were therefore unable to check all the information with the County Clubs. If in doubt, contact the Club a few days before the match.

Where we were not told if a facility exists, we have assumed it does not. Some international grounds who did not reply to our requests for information may have catering facilities, facilities for people with disabilities, etc but we have only included them if they have been confirmed to us.

Membership: It is important to check details with the County concerned. Full membership usually provides for free ground admission, except for National Westminster Trophy and Benson & Hedges knockout rounds, use of the pavilion and all members' facilities at the County's home grounds for all matches. There are also reciprocal arrangements for use of members' facilities when the member's County are playing away, subject to availabity, and after paying the ground admission fee.

Watching cricket outside Britain: We have covered how to find the Cricket Ground, and information about Cricket. We have not included other travel information, such as visa requirements, places to stay or safe areas in cities etc. We recommend using an established guide book. We apologise for the relative lack of information on Grounds in Pakistan - we hope to improve this section in a future edition.

Rapid Cricketline numbers: Calls charged at 45p per minute cheap rate, 50p per minute at all other times. Service provided by IMS Leeds LS1 8LB

There are bound to be mistakes in the book. We have visited every first class ground in England and Wales, but there can be changes that we are not aware of at the time of production. Please let us know any mistakes you find, so that we can make corrections in the future. Information about international grounds also very welcome. Please send comments or corrections to: London League Publications Ltd, P.O. Box 10441, London E14 0SB.

Please note that the authors and London League Publications Ltd do not accept any liability for any loss, injury or inconvenience sustained by people as a result of using the information or advice in this book.

INSIDE EDGE

THE NEW VOICE OF CRICKET

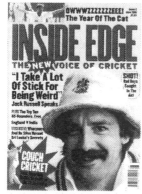

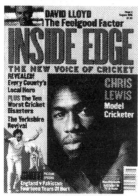

THE BRIGHTEST AND BEST CRICKET MAGAZINE AROUND

Available at all good newsagents or
call 0171 561 1606 for subscription details

Thank You

We would like to thank all the first class County Club officials, Minor Counties officials, officials and staff from grounds and clubs outside Britain, supporters' association officials, tourist information centre staff and travel information phone line staff who gave us information for this book. Sandra's consistent support and advice on tourism was very important. Amanda's hospitality and support were much appreciated. As well as the above, we would like to thank the following for their support:

David Armstrong (Minor Counties Cricket Association)
Mike Levene
Edward Osmond (Bloomberg Sports)
Graham Robertson
Samantha Sutherland (West Indies Cricket Board)
Fiona Walker (County Cricket Supporters Association)
Association of Sports Historians

British Association for Cricketers with Disabilities
Cricket Digest
Cricket Lore
Cricket Memorabilia Society
Cricket Society
Inside Edge
Lancashire CCC
Royal National Institute for the Blind
Wisden Cricket Monthly

All the advertisers, and everyone who subscribed to the book in advance.

Mike Atherton on the players' balcony at Lords (RO)

Contents

Great Britain:

The Pavilion, Harare (Giles Ridley)

The County Grounds

Lord's
MCC and Middlesex CCC

Description of ground: The mecca of cricket. Retaining its' great character and history. At its magnificent best when full for Test matches or cup finals. The Pavilion still only admits gentlemen. First staged cricket in 1814, and home to Middlesex CCC since 1877. Situated in residential St John's Wood, just north of the West End of London, and near Regent's Park.

Address: Lord's Ground, St Johns Wood Road, London, NW8 8QN.
Telephone:
MCC Secretariat: 0171-289-1611. Fax: 0171-289-9100
MCC Ticket enquiries: 0171-289-8979. Fax: 0171-266-3459
Prospects of play: 0171-286-8011
Lord's shop: 0171-432-1021
Gestetner Tours of Lord's: 0171-432-1033
Middlesex CCC: 0171-289-1300   *Membership:* 0171-286-5453
Middlesex CCC Shop: 0171-286-1310. Fax: 0171-289-5831.
Capacity: 28,000

General facilities:
Club shop: MCC at Nursery End. Middlesex behind pavilion,
Club museum: Yes - open match days only until 5.00 pm. In tennis court block behind pavilion.
Cricket coaching facilities: MCC Indoor school: 0171-432-1014/5. Middlesex have separate indoor school at Finchley.

Cricket nets: Indoor school. Outdoor nets (members only)
Other sporting or recreational facilities on the ground: Tennis court and squash courts (members only).
Facilities for hire or wider community use at the ground: Contact MCC for details

Facilities and access for people with disabilities:
Wheelchair access to the ground: Yes
Designated car parking available inside the ground: Yes (Not major matches)
Good viewing areas inside the ground for people using wheelchairs: Yes

Designated viewing areas: Yes, in Mound Stand and Warner Stand.
Ramps to provide easy access to bars and refreshment outlets: Yes

Food & drink:

	Members	**General Public**
Full restaurant/dining facilities:	Yes	Yes (not major matches)
Food suitable for vegetarians:	Yes	Yes
Bars: Not all open for all matches.	Yes	Yes

Travel:

Road restrictions on match days: All street parking is controlled. *Car parking:* Very limited at ground. Some private car parks nearby. Information: Master Park: 0800-243348. *Nearest station:* St John's Wood (London Underground).

Information: 0171-222-1234. *Buses:* 13, 82, 113, 139 and 274. Information: 0171-222-1234 *Tourist information:* 0839-123456 (premium rate). Tourist information centres at Victoria & Liverpool Street stations.

Road directions:

Lord's is on the A41, at the junction with St John's Wood Road (A5205). From central London, take the A501 inner ring road, and turn north at Gloucester Place (A41). This leads directly to Lord's. From the M1: at end of motorway turn left onto North Circular (A406). Stay in left hand lanes, and follow signs for A41, going onto roundabout, taking right turn onto A41. Stay on A41 until reaching Lord's. A1: stay on A1 until A41 forks off to right, then stay on A41.

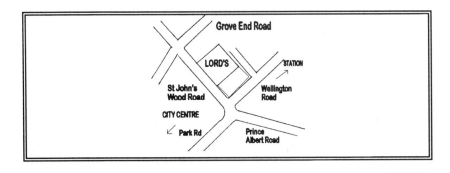

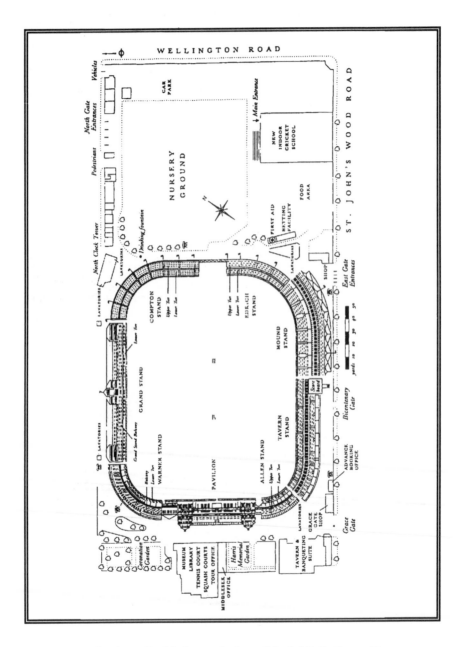

Lord's plan - By kind permission of the M.C.C. Committee

4

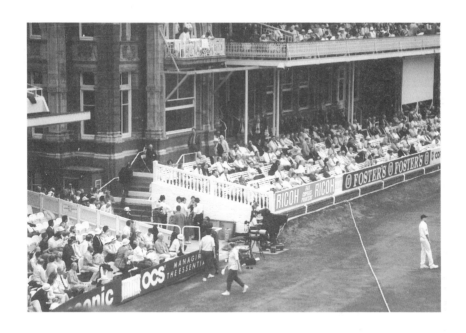

A streaker at Lord's (RO)

The new Mound Stand, Lord's (RO)

Derbyshire CCC

Club address: County Cricket Ground, Nottingham Road, Derby, Derbyshire, DE21 6DA
Telephone: 01332-383211   **Fax:** 01332-290251
Ticket Office: As above
Other telephone numbers:
Rapid Cricketline: 0891-567501
Grounds: Derby - County Cricket Ground
           Chesterfield Cricket Club - Queen's Park

1997 Membership Subscriptions:

Full	£75
Full (Country)	£48
Junior	£12
(Up to 18 on 1/1/97)	
Student	£39
Senior Citizen	£38
Senior Citizen (Country)	£29
Club/Firm	£225
Patron	£140
Patron (Country)	£90

Patron members receive a tickt, guest ticket & car park pass

Executive Individual (E1) £205
Member's ticket & car park pass, use of special facilities

Executive Individual (E2) £335
Member's ticket, guest ticket & 2 car park passes, use of special facilities

Executive Company (E4)
£625 (Plus VAT)
Member's ticket, 3 guest tickets (transferable) & 4 car park passes, use of special facilities

Car Park pass £35

Life membership also available.

Reciprocal arrangements:
On payment of admission charge, admission to Members' Enclosures or Pavilion at away matches involving Derbyshire CCC, (subject to local regulations).

Ground admission reductions given for:

Senior citizens:	Yes
School students:	Yes
Up to age:	16
Unemployed:	No
Students:	No

Family tickets available for AXA Equity and Law matches (2 adults & 2 children)

Supporters Club:
Derbyshire CCSC, County Cricket Ground, Nottingham Road, Derby, Derbyshire, DE21 6DA

Corporate entertaining:
Boxes and marquees available for all matches - contact Commercial Manager for details. Also, corporate facilities at County Ground.

Visually impaired people:
Reduced admission, helpers pay full price. Guide dogs allowed - contact club.

The County Ground - Derby (PDL)

Derbyshire CCC
County Ground: Derby

Description of ground: New pavilion and the Old Racecourse Stand combined with open seating. Only in recent years has it become the principal venue for Derbyshire's home matches. Built on the old Derby racecourse, and was for many years known as the Racecourse Ground.

Address: County Cricket Ground, Nottingham Road, Derby, DE21 6DA
Telephone: 01332-383211   **Capacity:** 9,000

General Facilities:

Club shop: Yes

Club museum: No

Cricket coaching facilities: Contact club.

Cricket nets: Yes

Other sporting or recreational facilities on the ground: Indoor

sports hall: 01332-383211.

Facilities for hire or wider community use at the ground: Contact club

Other sporting recreational / leisure activities: Football and cricket pitches by ground.

Facilities and access for people with disabilities:

Wheelchair access to the ground: Yes
Designated car parking available inside the ground: Yes
Good viewing areas inside the ground for people using wheelchairs: Yes
Designated viewing areas: No
Ramps to provide easy access to bars and refreshment outlets: Most accessible.

Food & drink:

	Members	General Public
Full restaurant/dining facilities:	Yes	Limited
Food suitable for vegetarians:	Yes	Yes
Bars:	2	2

Travel:

Car parking: £3.50.
Large car park at ground.
Nearest station: Derby.
Buses: 212. Bus station in town centre.Information: 01332-292200

Tourist information: Derby TIC, Assembly Rooms, Market Place, DE1 3AH. 01332-255802. Fax: 01332-256137.

Road directions:

By Pentagon roundabout, on A61(Sir Frank Whittle Road) and A52. Well signposted from Derby ring road.

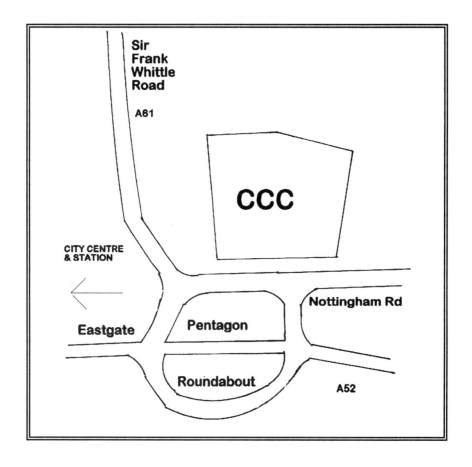

Derbyshire CCC
Chesterfield Cricket Club

Description of ground: Most attractive club ground in Queen's Park, with easy access, delightfully sited on a slope that runs down to the valley. Recreational atmosphere and the Cathedral with crooked spire to be glimpsed through the trees. Permanent seating and refreshment marquees to serve both members and public. Brown and Tunnicliffe once scored 554 in an opening partnership here for Yorkshire.

Address: Queen's Park, Boythorpe Avenue, Chesterfield, Derbyshire
Telephone: 01246-273090   **Capacity:** 7,000

General facilities:

Club shop: Yes
Club museum: No
Cricket coaching facilities: Contact club
Cricket nets: Contact club
Other sporting or recreational facilities on the ground: Athletics track, tennis club and bowling green in Queen's Park.
Facilities for hire or wider community use at the ground: In Queen's Park.

Facilities and access for people with disabilities:

Wheelchair access to the ground: Yes
Designated car parking available inside the ground: Contact club
Good viewing areas inside the ground for people using wheelchairs: Yes
Designated viewing areas: Yes
Ramps to provide easy access to bars and refreshment outlets: No

Food & drink:

	Members	General Public
Full restaurant/dining facilities:	No	No
Food suitable for vegetarians:	Yes	Yes
Bars:	1	1

10

Travel:

Car parking: Very limited at ground. Street parking and local car parks.

Nearest station: Chesterfield

Buses: Information: 01246-250450

Tourist information: Chesterfield TIC, Peacock Information Centre, S40 1PB. 01246-207777/8. Fax: 01246-556726

Road directions:

From A61, take turn off to A619 (Markham Rd) towards town centre. Turn left into Park Road, and ground is on right.

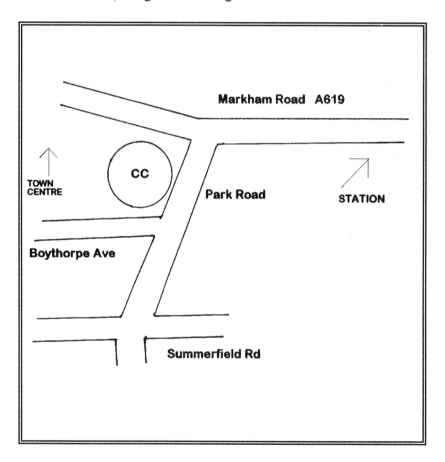

Durham CCC

Club address: County Ground, Riverside, Chester-le-Street, County Durham, DH3 3QR
Tel: 0191-387-1717   **Fax:** 0191-387-1616
Ticket Office: As above
Other telephone numbers:
0191-387-1418 (Match day number for Durham CCC office and shop at outgrounds)
Rapid Cricketline: 0891-567502
Grounds: Chester-le-Street - County Ground
Darlington Cricket Club
Hartlepool Cricket Club
Stockton Cricket Club

1997 Membership Subscriptions:

Full	£95
Full and spouse:	£160
Country:	£60
Country and spouse:	£100
Junior	£12
(Up to 18th birthday)	
Junior country:	£12
(Up to 18th birthday)	
Full-time student:	£45
(under 25)	
Senior (over 60):	£60
Senior & spouse:	£100
Senior country:	£40
Senior country & spouse:	£60
Family:	£175
Disabled:	£60
Overseas:	£35

Life membership also available.

Joint membership: 10% reduction on total fees for joint membership with Northumberland CCC or Cumberland CCC

Reciprocal arrangements:
Admission to members' areas at grounds where Durham are playing away.

Ground Admission reductions given for:

Senior citizens:	Yes
School students:	Yes
Up to age:	16
Unemployed:	No
Students:	No

Supporters Club:
C/o Marketing Department, Durham CCC.

Corporate entertaining:
Business Entertaining Package and Executive Hospitality Boxes available. Contact the club for details. Pavilion can be hired for conferences, product launches, wedding receptions etc.

Visually impaired people:
No reduced admission. Guide dogs allowed. No advance warning necessary.

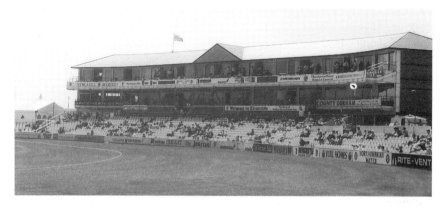

The Pavilion - County Ground, Chester-le-Street (PDL)

Hartlepool Cricket Club (PDL)

Durham CCC
County Ground: Chester-le-Street

Description of ground : Durham's permanent home after early nomadic first class years, although three other grounds still stage fixtures. Opened against Warwickshire on 18 May 1995, in bitterly cold weather! First ground in Britain to be specifically designed with Test cricket in mind. Built in modules - two completed so far, should hold 20,000 people when all five finished. Part of Riverside leisure area, with other sports facilities. Lumley Castle can be seen to the north east of the ground.

Address: Riverside, Chester-le-Street, County Durham, DH3 3QR
Telephone: 0191-387-1717   **Capacity:** 8,000

General facilities:
Club shop: Yes
Club museum: No
Cricket coaching facilities: Yes. In the winter in association with the Durham Cricket Association.
Cricket nets: Yes. In summer - selected members in conjunction with county squads.
Other sporting or recreational facilities on the ground: No. Next door is Riverside complex with other sporting facilities.

Facilities for hire or wider community use at the ground: Pavilion available all year round for hire for weddings, seminars, product launches etc.
Other sporting recreational / leisure activities: Separately run health club available to members and non members.

Facilities and access for people with disabilities:
Wheelchair access to the ground: Yes
Designated car parking available inside the ground: No
Good viewing areas inside the ground for people using wheelchairs: Yes
Designated viewing areas: Yes
Ramps to provide easy access to bars and refreshment outlets: Yes

Food & drink:

	Members	General Public
Full restaurant/dining facilities:	Yes	Yes
Food suitable for vegetarians:	Yes	Yes
Bars:	2	1

Travel:

Car parking: Members & General Public: £2. Ample parking in vicinity of Ground.
Nearest station: Chester-le-Street (information: 0191-2326262)

Buses: 778, 775, 734. Information: 0191-386-4411 x 3337
Tourist information: Durham TIC, Market Place, Durham, 0191-384-3720.

Road directions:

From A1(M) junction 63, take A167 (Shields Road) south from roundabout. Stay on A167 at roundabout, which becomes Park Road North, then Park Road Central. Left at roundabout into Ropery Lane, then right, into Riverside complex.

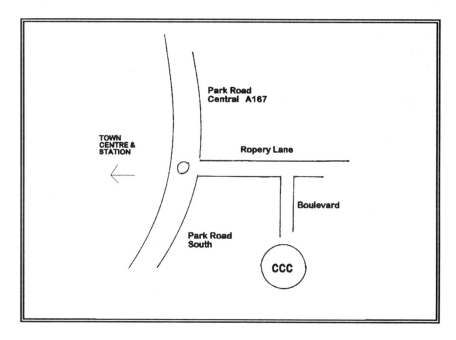

Durham CCC
Darlington Cricket Club

Description: Club ground adjoining Darlington Football Club. The floodlights and football stand provide a background to the cricket. Pavilion and some permanent seating. Near town centre, next to new supermarket.

Address: Feethams Cricket Ground, South Terrace, Darlington, DL1 5JD
Telephone: 01325-466415   **Capacity:** 5,000

General facilities:
Club shop: Yes
Club museum: No
Cricket coaching facilities: Contact the club.
Cricket nets: Contact the club.
Other sporting or recreational facilities on the ground: Hockey. Darlington FC adjoins ground.
Facilities for hire or wider community use at the ground: Contact club.

Facilities and access for people with disabilities:
Wheelchair access to the ground: Yes
Designated car parking available inside the ground: Contact club.
Good viewing areas inside the ground for people using wheelchairs: Yes
Designated viewing areas: Yes
Ramps to provide easy access to bars and refreshment outlets: Yes

Food & drink:

	Members	General Public
Full restaurant/dining facilities:	No	No
Food suitable for vegetarians:	Yes	Yes
Bars:	3	2

Travel:
Car parking: Very limited at ground. Street parking and town centre car parks
Nearest station: Darlington
Buses: Depot very near ground.
Information: *01325-468771*

16

Tourist information: Darlington   01325-388666.
TIC, 13, Horsemarket, DL1 5PW.   Fax: 01325-388667

Road directions:

From A66, take A167 (Grange Rd) towards town centre. Turn right onto Victoria Rd (still A167- dual carriageway), and ground is on right, next to supermarket. Turn round at next roundabout for access.

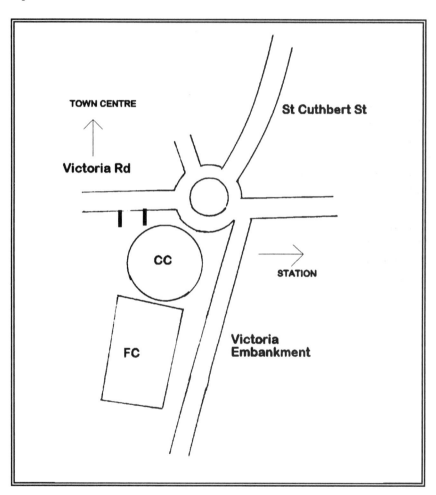

Durham CCC
Hartlepool Cricket Club

Description of ground: Council owned club ground. Pleasant setting. Used by Hartlepool CC since 1855 - according to the clock on the pavilion. Near parks outside town centre.

Address: The Pavilion, Park Drive, West Park, Hartlepool, TS26 0DA
Telephone: 012429-260875   **Capacity:** 3,500

General facilities:
Club shop: Yes
Club museum: No
Cricket coaching facilities:
Contact Hartlepool CC
Cricket nets: Yes

Other sporting or recreational facilities on the ground: None
Facilities for hire or wider community use at the ground:
Contact Hartlepool CC.

Facilities and access for people with disabilities:
Wheelchair access to the ground: Yes
Designated car parking available inside the ground: Contact club.
Good viewing areas inside the ground for people using wheelchairs: Yes
Designated viewing areas: No
Ramps to provide easy access to bars and refreshment outlets: No

Food & drink:

	Members	General Public
Full restaurant/dining facilities:	No	No
Food suitable for vegetarians:	No	No
Bars:	1	1

Travel:
Car parking: Very limited at ground. Street parking and at local schools.
Nearest station: Hartlepool
Buses: Information: 0191-386-

4411 x3337
Tourist information: Hartlepool TIC, Hartlepool Art Gallery, Church Sq, TS24 7EQ.
01429-266522. Fax:01429-856450

Road directions:

From A689 (Stockton St), turn left into Park Rd. Turn right at T junction into Elwick Rd, and immediately left (still Elwick Rd). Pass Ward Jackson Park on right, turn right (still Elwick Rd) and ground is on left.

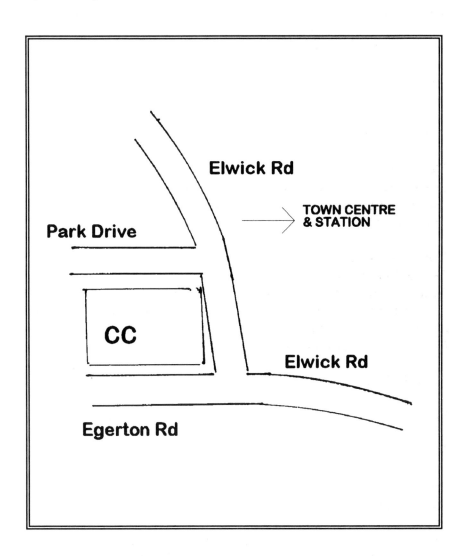

Durham CCC
Stockton Cricket Club

Description: Attractive club ground with modern pavilion and scoreboard. Outside town centre. Club founded in 1816.

Address: The Grangefield Road Ground, Oxbridge Avenue, Stockton-on-Tees, TS18 4JF
Telephone: 01642-672835   **Capacity:** 4,000

General facilities:
Club shop: Yes
Club museum: No
Cricket coaching facilities: Yes
Indoor winter nets - contact Stockton CC
Cricket nets: Yes
Other sporting or recreational facilities on the ground: Hockey and croquet.
Facilities for hire or wider community use at the ground: None

Facilities and access for people with disabilities:
Wheelchair access to the ground: Yes
Designated car parking available inside the ground: No
Good viewing areas inside the ground for people using wheelchairs: Yes
Designated viewing areas: Yes
Ramps to provide easy access to bars and refreshment outlets: Yes

Food & drink:

	Members	General Public
Full restaurant/dining facilities:	No	No
Food suitable for vegetarians:	Yes	Yes
Bars:	3	2

Travel:
Car parking: Members & general public: £2. Additional parking provided - very limited at ground.

Nearest station: Stockton
Buses: Information: 0191-386-4411 x3337

Tourist information: Stockton on Tees TIC, Theatre Yard, Off High St, TS18 1AT. 01642-615080. Fax:01642-616315.

Road directions:

From town centre: A135 towards Yarm. Fork right into Oxbridge Lane (signposted local). Next roundabout turn right (signposted Norton A1027) into Oxbridge Avenue. Ground on right, opposite Grangefield School. From A66, take A135 (Yarm Rd) towards town centre, turn left into Oxbridge Lane, then as above.

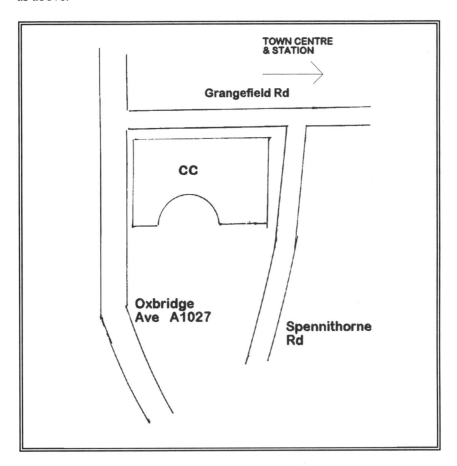

Essex CCC

Club address: The County Ground, New Writtle Street, Chelmsford, Essex, CM2 0PG
Telephone: 01245-252420   **Fax:** 01245-491607
Ticket Office: As above
Other telephone numbers:
Essex Rapid Cricketline: 0891-567503
Cricket school: 01245-266794
Ticket information and prospects for play: 01245-287921 (answerphone)
Grounds: Chelmsford - County Ground
            Colchester - Colchester & East Essex CC - Castle Park
            Ilford - Ilford CC - Valentine's Park
            Southend - Southend on Sea CC - Southchurch Park

1997 Membership Subscriptions:

Full:	£67
Husband & wife:	£118
Junior:	£18
(under 18)	
Student:	£26

(Age 18 - 22 in full-time education)

Senior:	£39.50
Senior husband & wife:	£70
Corporate patron - per ticket:	£76
Club - per ticket:	£77
Executive Suite (Individual):	£146

(Plus membership at appropriate rate)

Executive Suite (Corporate): £690 (Two transferable tickets - joining fee also payable)

Life membership also available.

Disabled members who cannot watch without a carer are entitled to apply for a free ticket for their carer.

Free car parking for members when available

Reciprocal arrangements:
Admission to designated Member's enclosures on other grounds when Essex are playing (on payment of ground admission). Some counties restrict this facility for visiting members.

Ground admission reductions given for:

Senior citizens:	Yes
School students:	Yes
Up to age:	18
Unemployed:	Yes
(Championship matches only)	
Students:	No

Other: Groups of school children, the disabled, disadvantaged, etc. (Usually only championship matches at management's request. Contact the Club for details)

Supporters Club:
The Boundary Club, c/o Essex CCC - as above. Contact: Malcolm Rowley 01245- 284929.

Junior members club:
Essex Cricket Cadets - free to junior members

Corporate entertaining:
Personal business entertaining plans available. Contact the Marketing Department for details. Facilities for hire also available at County Ground.

Visually impaired people:
No reduced admission. Guide dogs allowed. Contact club in advance.

On the road - the Essex mobile scoreboard at Southend (PDL)

Essex CCC
County Ground: Chelmsford

Description of ground: Modernised ground. One of the best County Grounds outside the Test match arenas. Next door to Chelmsford City FC. Used by Essex since 1933, and became the County Ground in 1965. In attractive town centre setting next to Central Park and the river Can.

Address: New Writtle Street, Chelmsford, Essex, CM2 0PG
Telephone: 01245-252420   **Capacity:** 7,000

General facilities:
Club shop: Yes
Club museum: Yes
Cricket coaching facilities: Yes. Available all year in indoor school.
Cricket nets: Yes
Other sporting or recreational facilities on the ground: No
Facilities for hire or wider community use at the ground: Rooms for weddings, exhibitions, conferences etc.

Facilities and access for people with disabilities:
Wheelchair access to the ground: Yes
Designated car parking available inside the ground: Yes
Good viewing areas inside the ground for people using wheelchairs: Yes
Designated viewing areas: Yes
Ramps to provide easy access to bars and refreshment outlets: Yes

Food & drink:

	Members	General Public
Full restaurant/dining facilities:	Yes	No
Food suitable for vegetarians:	Yes	Yes
Bars:	2	1

Travel:
Car parking: Free for members at ground (limited space). Town centre car parks.

Nearest station: Chelmsford.
Buses: Bus station 0.5 miles from ground. Information: 0345-000333

Tourist information: Chelmsford TIC, E Block, County Hall, Market Rd, CM1 1GG. 01245-283400. Fax: 01245-515535.

Road directions:

Ground is in town centre, near the junction of the A138 with the B1007 (New London Road). Access by car is from the B1007, and then turn into New Writtle Street. The ground is next door to Chelmsford City FC

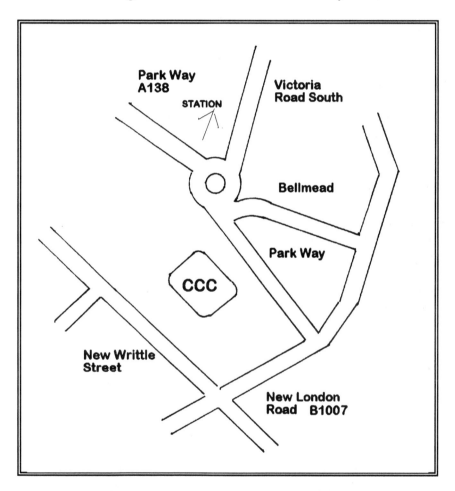

Essex CCC
Colchester & East Essex CC

Description of ground: Club ground in Castle Park, next door to Leisure World centre. First used by Essex in 1914, then in the 1930s, and regularly since 1946. Pleasant setting for summer festival week with spectators close enough to feel involved rather than detached in remote stands.

Address: Castle Park (Lower), Sports Way, Colchester, Essex
Telephone: 01206-574028 **Capacity:** 6,000

General facilities:
Club shop: Yes
Club museum: No
Cricket coaching facilities: Contact club.
Cricket nets: Contact club
Other sporting or recreational facilities on the ground: Hockey.

Facilities for hire or wider community use at the ground: None.
Other sporting recreational / leisure activities: Leisure World centre nearby.

Facilities and access for people with disabilities:
Wheelchair access to the ground: Yes
Designated car parking available inside the ground: Yes
Good viewing areas inside the ground for people using wheelchairs: Yes
Designated viewing areas: Yes
Ramps to provide easy access to bars and refreshment outlets: No

Food & drink:

	Members	General Public
Full restaurant/dining facilities:	Yes	No
Food suitable for vegetarians:	Yes	Yes
Bars:	1	1

Travel:
Car parking: Large car park in ground, members free, public £2.

Nearest station: Colchester St. Botolph's or Colchester North.

Buses: Bus station off High Street, 0.75 miles from ground. Information: Eastern National: 01206-571451, Colchester Borough Transport: 01206-764029

Tourist information: Colchester TIC, 1, Queen St, CO1 2PG. 01206-282920. Fax: 01206-282924.

Road directions:
Take A133 from A12. This becomes Colne Bank Avenue. Go straight over roundabout with A134. Follow signs for Leisure World, but before reaching there, take next right into Catchpool Road. This leads into Sports Way, by ground.

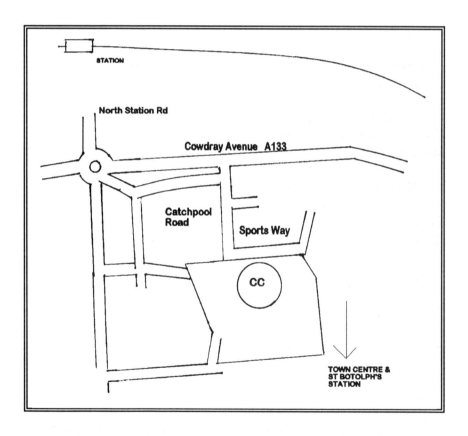

Essex CCC
Ilford Cricket Club

Description of ground: Club ground set in public park. First used by Essex in the 1920s. In suburban east London, unlike other Essex grounds based in towns around the county. Essex grounds hold small crowds, but they have responded to the enterprises and successes of the County and love their cricket.

Address: Valentine's Park, Cranbrook Road, Ilford, Essex
Telephone: 0181-554-8381   **Capacity:** 5,000

General facilities
Club shop: Yes
Club museum: No
Cricket coaching facilities: Contact club.
Cricket nets: Contact club.
Other sporting or recreational

facilities on the ground: No.
Facilities for hire or wider community use at the ground: No.
Other sporting recreational / leisure activities: Tennis and bowls in the park.

Facilities and access for people with disabilities
Wheelchair access to the ground: Yes
Designated car parking available inside the ground: Yes
Good viewing areas inside the ground for people using wheelchairs: Yes
Designated viewing areas: Yes
Ramps to provide easy access to bars and refreshment outlets: No

Food & drink:

	Members	General Public
Full restaurant/dining facilities:	Yes	No
Food suitable for vegetarians:	Yes	Yes
Bars:	2	1

Travel:
Car parking: None at ground. Field in park for members & public.
Nearest station: Ilford (train) or Gants Hill (underground)

Buses: 123,129,144,150,167,179, 247 & 296 all pass Ilford or Gants Hill stations.
Information: 0171-222-1234

Tourist information:
Redbridge TIC, Town Hall, High   Rd, IG1 1DD. 0181-478-3020.
Fax: 0181-478-9149

Road directions:

A12 Gants Hill roundabout   (i.e. with A1400 and A123): take A123
(Cranbrook Road) south from roundabout - signposted Ilford & Barking.
Ground is on left hand side, around 0.5 miles from roundabout.

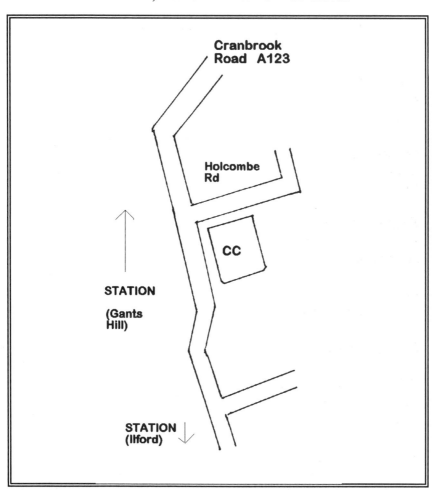

Essex CCC
Southend-on-Sea CC

Description of ground: In public park, next to athletics track. There is also a boating lake behind the ground. First used by Essex in 1906, now the only ground the County use in Southend. Very near the sea. Marquees and temporary seating take over in County matches, and look out for the mobile scoreboard in a van - a feature of Essex on the road.

Address: Southchurch Park, Northumberland Crescent, Southend on Sea
Telephone: 01702-615195 (County matches only) **Capacity:** 6,000

General facilities:

Club shop: Yes
Club museum: No
Cricket coaching facilities: Contact club.
Cricket nets: Contact club.

Other sporting or recreational facilities on the ground: Hockey. Athletics stadium next door.
Facilities for hire or wider community use at the ground: No.

Facilities and access for people with disabilities:
Wheelchair access to the ground: Yes
Designated car parking available inside the ground: Yes
Good viewing areas inside the ground for people using wheelchairs: Yes
Designated viewing areas: Yes
Ramps to provide easy access to bars and refreshment outlets: No

Food & drink:

	Members	General Public
Full restaurant/dining facilities:	Yes	No
Food suitable for vegetarians:	Yes	Yes
Bars:	1	1

Travel:
Car parking: Some at ground -free for members. Otherwise £2 at Lifstan Road car park.

Nearest station: Southend East
Buses: Eastern National 20, Shoeburyness to Hullbridge passes

train stations Southend Central and Victoria. 7, 8, 9, 67 and 68. Information: Southend Public Transport: 01702-434444, Thamesway: 01268-525251

Tourist information: Southend-on-Sea TIC, 19, High St, SS1 1JE. 01702-215120. Fax: 01702-431449.

Road directions:

Ground is to the east of town centre. Take A13 (Southchurch Rd) from town centre, turn right onto Lifstan Way, and ground is on right. Alternative: drive along sea front - Eastern Esplanade (B1016) and turn left into Lifstan Way.

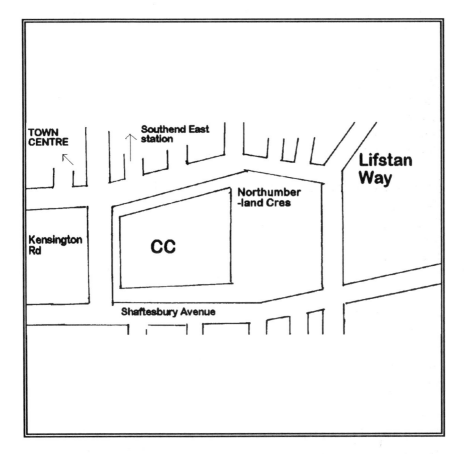

Glamorgan CCC

Club address: Sophia Gardens, Cardiff, CF1 9XR
Telephone: 01222-343478 **Fax:** 01222-377044
Ticket Office: As above
Other telephone numbers:
Rapid Cricketline: 0891-567504
Grounds: Cardiff - Sophia Gardens
Abergavenny - Abergavenny CC - Pen-y-Pound ground
Colwyn Bay - Colwyn Bay CC - Penrhyn Avenue
Pontypridd - Pontypridd CC - Ynysangharad Park
Swansea - Swansea Cricket & Football Club - St Helens ground

1997 Membership Subscriptions:
Full:	£25
Junior (Short legs):	£10
Up to age: 17 & under at 1/4/97	
Students:	No reductions
Senior citizens:	No reductions
Gold Member:	£35
(as for full, includes monthly draw)	
Gold Vice President:	£70

(As for Gold Member, free admission to tourist matches & other facilities)

Affiliated Club: £60
(Transferable ticket as for Gold V P. Affiliated Clubs only)

Premier Club: £1,250
(10 yr membership, other privileges)

Reciprocal arrangements:
Subject to availability, use of members' facilities at Worcester, Somerset and Gloucestershire. Away matches, use of members' facilities after paying admission, subject to availability.

Ground admission reductions given for:
Senior citizens:	Yes
School students:	Yes
Up to age:	16
Unemployed:	No
Students:	No

Supporters Club:
St. Helens Balconiers, c/o Mr Philip L. James (Secretary) 36, Whitestone Avenue, Swansea SA3 3DA. Tel/Fax: 01792-232325.

Corporate entertaining:
Cardiff:Marquees, suites. Swansea: suites.Colwyn Bay:Marquees. Contact Marketing Department.

Visually impaired people:
No reduced admission. Guide dogs allowed.

Rain stopped play at Sophia Gardens (RO)

Cricket in the sun at Swansea (RO)

Glamorgan CCC
Cardiff: Sophia Gardens

Description of ground: Glamorgan first played at Sophia Gardens in 1967 against the Indian tourists and now own the ground close to the River Taff and in a delightful tree surrounded rural setting. Near city centre, and next door to Welsh Institute of Sport. The County has recently unveiled ambitious plans to develop the ground into a National Cricket Ground for Wales

Address: Sophia Gardens, Cardiff, CF1 9XR
Telephone: 01222-343478
Capacity: 5,500 (plus temporary seating as necessary)

General facilities:
Club shop: Yes
Club museum: Yes (not match days)
Cricket coaching facilities: Yes (not match days)
Cricket nets: Yes (players only)
Other sporting or recreational facilities on the ground: Hockey.
Facilities for hire or wider community use at the ground: No
Other sporting recreational / leisure activities: Tennis courts and other facilities next door, at Welsh Institute of Sport.

Facilities and access for people with disabilities:
Wheelchair access to the ground: Yes
Designated car parking available inside the ground: Yes
Good viewing areas inside the ground for people using wheelchairs: Yes
Designated viewing areas: Yes
Ramps to provide easy access to bars and refreshment outlets: Yes

Food & drink:

	Members	General Public
Full restaurant/dining facilities:	Yes	No
Food suitable for vegetarians:	Yes	Yes
Bars:	3	2

34

Travel:

Car parking: Field next to ground, or at Sports Centre complex

Nearest station: Cardiff Central, 1 mile from ground

Buses: 32, 62 from station. Also 25, 33, 21. Information: 01222-396521. Also other buses to Cathedral Road.

Tourist information: Cardiff Central Station, Central Square, Cardiff CF1 1QY. 01222-227281

Road directions:

On Cathedral Road (A4119), just north of junction with A4161. From M4, junction 29, A48 towards city centre. Turn off A48 onto A4161 towards city centre, follow the signs over the Taff Bridge and filter right to Cathedral Road.

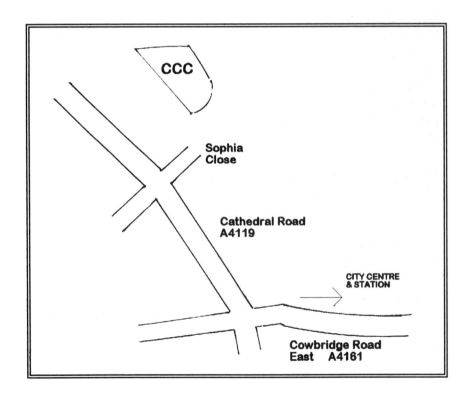

Glamorgan CCC
Abergavenny Cricket Club

Description of ground: The Abergavenney Cricket Club ground was first used in 1834. Known as Pen-y-Pound, it has been staging championship cricket since 1983. Surrounded by hills - Deri, Blorenge and Skirrid, it is the perfect setting for a day at the cricket.

Address: Pen-y-Pound Cricket Ground, Avenue Road, Abergavenny, Gwent
Telephone: 01873-852350   **Capacity:** 5,000

General facilities:
Club shop: Yes

Club museum: No

Cricket coaching facilities: No

Cricket nets: No

Other sporting or recreational facilities on the ground: No

Facilities for hire or wider community use at the ground: No

Other sporting recreational or leisure activities: Bowls and tennis in park.

Facilities and access for people with disabilities:
Wheelchair access to the ground: Yes - contact club
Designated car parking available inside the ground: Contact club
Good viewing areas inside the ground for people using wheelchairs: Yes
Designated viewing areas: No
Ramps to provide easy access to bars and refreshment outlets: No

Food & drink:

	Members	General Public
Full restaurant/dining facilities:	Yes	No
Food suitable for vegetarians:	Yes	Yes
Bars:	2	1

Travel:
Car parking: Limited at ground. Additional parking at football ground, and street parking.

Nearest station: Abergavenny
Buses: Bus station 1.5 miles from ground, by Tourist Information

36

Office. 21to end of Pen-Y-Pound   Abergavenny TIC, Swan Meadow,
Information: 01633-266336   Monmouth Rd, NP7 5HH.
Tourist information: 01873 -857588

Road directions:

From roundabout of A40 with Merthyr Road by pass and Mount Street, go towards town centre. Turn left into Chapel Road, right into Harold Road which leads into Avenue Road. For parking, turn left into Pen-y-Pound for football ground. Access also from Old Hereford Rd. From Heads of the Valleys Road, (A465), take A4143 Merthyr Road towards town centre, at roundabout take first turning into Merthyr Road by pass, right at roundabout, then as above.

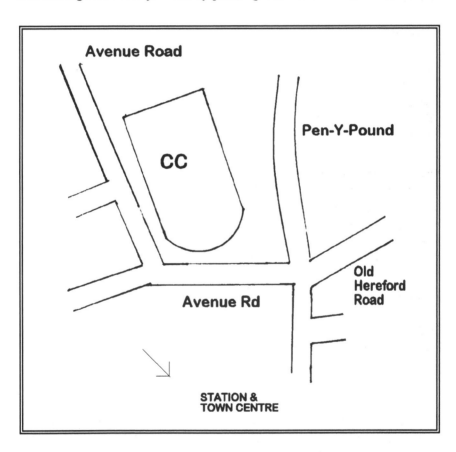

Glamorgan CCC
Colwyn Bay Cricket Club

Description of ground: Agreeable ground used by Glamorgan and well attended by cricket followers in North Wales since 1966. Modern pavilion. Banking on two sides of ground provide good viewing areas. Near the town centre and the sea. Also used by Wales for Minor Counties matches.

Address: Penrhyn Avenue, Rhos-on-Sea, Colwyn Bay, Clwyd LL28 4LR
Telephone: 01492-544103 or 545082
Capacity: 4,750 with temporary seating

General facilities:
Club shop: Yes
Club museum: No
Cricket coaching facilities: No
Cricket nets: No
Other sporting or recreational facilities on the ground: No

Facilities for hire or wider community use at the ground: Midland Bank suite for dinners etc.
Other sporting recreational or leisure activities: Bowls next door. Hockey.

Facilities and access for people with disabilities:
Wheelchair access to the ground: Yes
Designated car parking available inside the ground: Contact club
Good viewing areas inside the ground for people using wheelchairs: Yes
Designated viewing areas: Yes
Ramps to provide easy access to bars and refreshment outlets: No

Food & drink:

	Members	General Public
Full restaurant/dining facilities:	No	No
Food suitable for vegetarians:	No	No
Bars:	1	1

Travel:
Car parking: Limited at ground. Additional parking provided, and street parking.
Nearest station: Colwyn Bay.

38

Information: 0345-484950
Buses: 12,16 or any towards
Llandudno. Stop by ground.
Information: 01492-596969.

Tourist information: Colwyn Bay
TIC, 40 Station Rd, LL29 8BU.
01492-530478.
Fax: 01492-534789

Road directions:

Ground is in Rhos-on-Sea, rather than Colwyn Bay. From Colwyn Baytown centre, take promenade north towards Rhos-on-Sea. Turn left into Penrhyn Avenue. From A55, take turning signposted Rhos on Sea, follow signs for Rhos-on-Sea. At roundabout, turn into Brompton Avenue, right at traffic lights into Rhos Road, left into Colwyn Crescent, and left into Penrhyn Avenue.

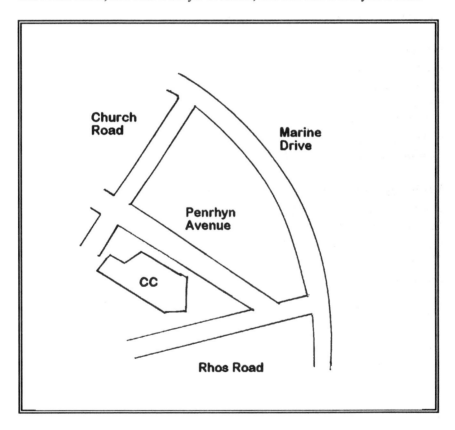

Glamorgan CCC
Pontypridd Cricket Club

Description of ground: Attractive club ground set in public park, with locals welcoming a County cricket match as the highlight of the season. By River Taff and near town centre.

Address: Pontypridd CC, The Pavilion, Ynysangharad Park, Pontypridd
Telephone: 01443-400785   **Capacity:** 5,000 (with temporary seating)

General facilities:
Club shop: Yes
Club museum: No
Cricket coaching facilities: Contact club
Cricket nets: Contact club
Other sporting or recreational

facilities on the ground: Football
Other sporting recreational / leisure activities: Tennis courts, swimming, football and rugby union in the park.

Facilities and access for people with disabilities:
Wheelchair access to the ground: Yes
Designated car parking available inside the ground: Contact club
Good viewing areas inside the ground for people using wheelchairs: Yes
Designated viewing areas: No
Ramps to provide easy access to bars and refreshment outlets: No

Food & drink:

	Members	General Public
Full restaurant/dining facilities:	No	No
Food suitable for vegetarians:	No	No
Bars:	1	1

Travel:
Car parking: Very limited at ground. Some street parking and local car parks.

Nearest station: Pontypridd. Information: 0345-484950
Buses: Bus station in town centre

40

5, C19, 132, 244 to Taff St.
Information:
Rhondda:01443-682671,
Caerphilly: 01222-867003,
Shamrock: 01443-407000

Tourist information: Pontypridd
Historical and Cultural Centre, The
Old Bridge, CF37 4PE
01443-409512.
Fax: 01443-485565

Road directions:
A470 take turning for Pontypridd inner relief road, signposted Pontypridd. Use
local car parks, and ground is across bridge from Taff Street.

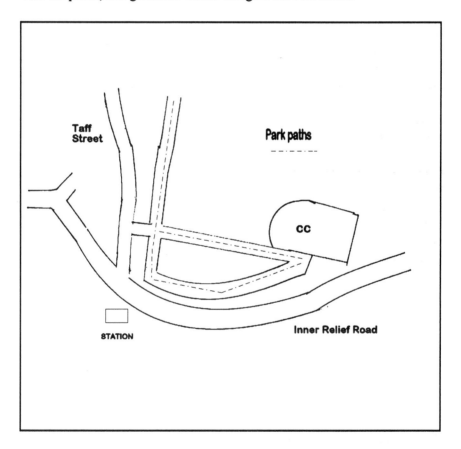

Glamorgan CCC
Swansea Cricket & Football Club

Description of ground: Glamorgan first played here in 1921. The Ground where in August 1968, Sobers scored six sixes in an over. A Rugby Ground with the pavilion high up on the terracing and the football stand opposite. A minute from the beach and views over Swansea Bay. Lovely in the sunshine, but find comfort in the pavilion when cold winds blow.

Address: Swansea Cricket and Football Club, St Helen's Cricket Ground, Bryn Road, Swansea, West Glamorgan SA2 0AR
Telephone: 01792-424242   **Capacity:** 3,750 plus temporary seating

General facilities:
Club shop: Yes
Club museum: No
Cricket coaching facilities: No
Cricket nets: No
Other sporting or recreational facilities on the ground: Rugby Union
Facilities for hire or wider community use at the ground: None

Facilities and access for people with disabilities:
Wheelchair access to the ground: Yes
Designated car parking available inside the ground: No
Good viewing areas inside the ground for people using wheelchairs: Yes
Designated viewing areas: No
Ramps to provide easy access to bars and refreshment outlets: Yes

Food & drink:

	Members	General Public
Full restaurant/dining facilities:	Yes	No
Food suitable for vegetarians:	Yes	Yes
Bars:	2	1

Travel:

Car parking: None at ground. Local car parks, and street parking. *Nearest station:* Swansea 1.5 miles *Buses:* 1, 2, 3, from bus station. Information: 01792-580580

Tourist information: Swansea Tourist Information Centre, PO Box 59, Singleton St, Swansea SA1 3QG 01792-468321

Road directions: From city centre take Oystermouth Road along coast (A4067), heading west. Pass County Hall on left. This road becomes Mumbles Road. Ground on right. No AA signs but aim for the Mumbles. Limited parking opposite, but much more a bit further on.

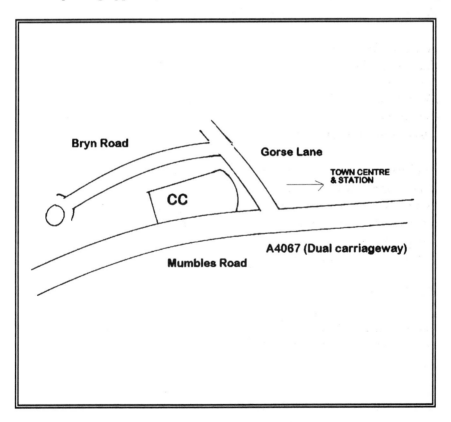

Gloucestershire CCC

Club address: Sun Alliance County Ground, Nevil Road, Bristol, BS7 9EJ
Telephone: 0117-924-5216   **Fax:** 0117-924-1193
Ticket Office: As above
Other telephone numbers:
County Cashline: 0117-942-8180
Marketing: 0117-942-8180
Catering Manager: 0117-942-3024
Rapid Cricketline: 0891-567505
Grounds: Bristol - Sun Alliance County Ground
         Gloucester - King's School
         Cheltenham - Cheltenham College

1997 Membership Subscriptions:
Full single:	£69
Full single (country):	£64
Husband & wife:	£95
Husband & wife (country):	£85

(With separate membership cards & use of facilities)
Child (14 & under):	£10
Junior / Student:	£24

(18 or under, or 21 & under with student card)
Senior citizen:	£38
Senior citizen (country):	£35
Senior citizen (husband & wife):	£53
Senior citizen (husband & wife) - (Country):	£49
Country (Husband & wife):	£55
Affiliated club:(sports & other)	£65

(2 transferable tickets)
Business Patrons: (5 tickets)	£150
Business Patrons: (10 tickets)	£250
Ground season ticket	
(club cricketers):	£10

Life membership also available.
Parking:	£20

Country membership: Outside 20 miles radius of county HQ.

Reciprocal arrangements: Use of members' areas at Glamorgan, Somerset and Worcestershire. Use of members facilities at away matches, after paying admission, subject to availablity

Ground admission reductions given for:
Senior citizens:	Yes
School students:	Yes
Up to age:	16
Unemployed:	No
Students:	Yes

Supporters Club: None

Visually impaired people: No reduced admission, guide dogs allowed

Corporate entertaining: Facilities available at matches. Contact club for details

3 ladies at Bristol (RO)

Cheltenham College cricket (RO)

Gloucestershire CCC
Sun Alliance County Ground: Bristol

Description of ground: High up on the northern side of the city, the ground is surrounded by houses and the former Muller orphanage buildings, now the City of Bristol College. The historical importance of the ground where Grace, Jessop and Hammond once thrilled West Country cricket lovers amply compensates for the undistinguished sprawl of buildings from the late nineteenth century pavilion, via terracing to the Jessop Tavern. There is a new press box and shop and office block at the Nevil Road end to be ready for the new season.

Address: Sun Alliance County Ground, Nevil Road, Bristol, BS7 9EJ
Telephone: 0117-924-5216   **Capacity:** 4,500

General facilities:
Club shop: Yes
Club museum: Yes
Cricket coaching facilities: Yes
Cricket nets: Yes - all year
Other sporting or recreational facilities on the ground: Squash, gym, tennis.

Facilities for hire or wider community use at the ground: Yes - contact club
Other sporting recreational or leisure activities: Yes - contact club

Facilities and access for people with disabilities:
Wheelchair access to the ground: Yes
Designated car parking available inside the ground: Yes
Good viewing areas inside the ground for people using wheelchairs: Yes
Designated viewing areas: No
Ramps to provide easy access to bars and refreshment outlets: Yes

Food & drink:

	Members	**General Public**
Full restaurant/dining facilities:	Yes	No
Food suitable for vegetarians:	Yes	Yes
Bars:	2	1

Travel:

Car parking: Inside ground.
Nearest station: Bristol Parkway or Bristol Temple Meads
Buses: From Bristol Fashion (by bus station): 72,73,74,75,76 and 77. From Bristol Parkway: 72 & 73. From Bristol Temple Meads: 8 & 9 to bus station, then as above.
Information: 0117-955-5111
Tourist information: Bristol TIC, St Nicholas Church, St Nicholas St, BS1 1UE. Tel: 0117-926-0767. Fax: 0117- 929-7703.

Road directions:

M32 take junction 2, for Fishponds and Horfield. Take Muller Road exit (3rd if coming from M4). Turn left into Ralph Rd (turning opposite bus station). Turn left at end of road onto Ashley Down Rd, then almost immediately right into Kennington Avenue. Turn left at end of road to ground. Not easy to find at first, there will be more permanent road signs for 1997.

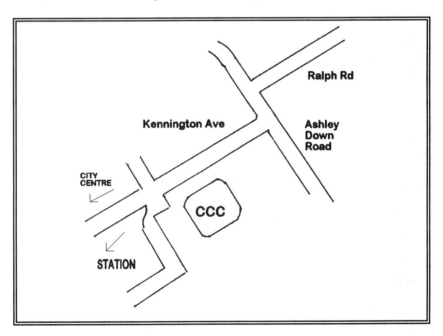

Gloucestershire CCC
Cheltenham College

Description of ground: County cricket in the leafy splendour of the Cheltenham College ground has been enjoyed since 1872 when Grace took 12 wickets against Surrey, and is one of the delights of the summer. Marquees around the ground, with deck chairs and temporary stands, it is cricket in the holiday season with a festival atmosphere.

Address: College Sports Ground, Cheltenham College, Thirlestaine Road, Cheltenham
Telephone: 01242-522000   **Capacity:** 4,000

General facilities:
Club shop: Yes
Club museum: No
Cricket coaching facilities: No
Cricket nets: No
Other sporting or recreational

facilities on the ground: No
Facilities for hire or wider community use at the ground: None

Facilities and access for people with disabilities
Wheelchair access to the ground: Yes - contact club
Designated car parking available inside the ground: Yes - contact club
Good viewing areas inside the ground for people using wheelchairs: Yes
Designated viewing areas: No
Ramps to provide easy access to bars and refreshment outlets: Not necessary - all at ground level

Food & drink:

	Members	General Public
Full restaurant/dining facilities:	Yes	Yes
Food suitable for vegetarians:	Yes	Yes
Bars:	1	Numerous

Travel:

Car parking:£3.00 in ground or at overflow (400 yds away).
Nearest station: Cheltenham Spa (1 mile)
Buses: L to Bath Road.

Information: 01242-522021
Tourist information: Cheltenham TIC, 77, Promenade, GL50 1PP. 01242-522878.
Fax: 01242-515535

Road directions: The ground is situated south of the town centre. Thirlestaine Road is off the A46 (Bath Road). Well signed routes from the M5 and good on ground parking with overspill nearby for late arrivals.

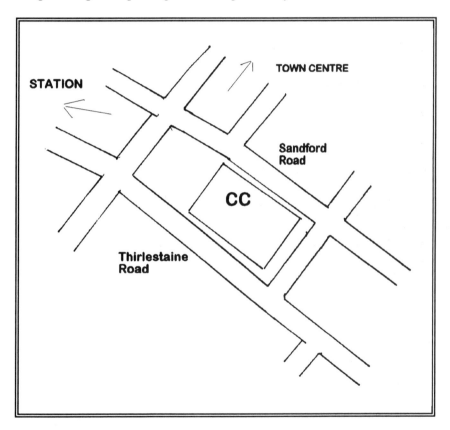

Gloucestershire CCC
King's School, Gloucester

Description of ground: The ground is within walking distance of the cathedral and city centre. It has been hosting championship cricket since replacing the Wagon Works ground in 1993. Archdeacon Meadow is built on the site of an old rubbish tip within which are buried two double decker buses and parts of several tanks ! ! But poplars loom and spectators stroll around enjoying the intimate friendliness of a small country ground.

Address: Archdeacon Meadow, King's School, St Oswald's Road, Gloucester
Telephone: 01452-423011   **Capacity:** 2,500

General facilities:
Club shop: Yes
Club museum: No
Cricket coaching facilities: No
Cricket nets: No
Other sporting or recreational

facilities on the ground: Tennis courts. Pitch & putt golf and Leisure centre by ground.
Facilities for hire or wider community use at the ground: No

Facilities and access for people with disabilities:
Wheelchair access to the ground: Yes - contact club
Designated car parking available inside the ground: Yes
Good viewing areas inside the ground for people using wheelchairs: Yes
Designated viewing areas: No
Ramps to provide easy access to bars and refreshment outlets: No

Food & drink:

	Members	General Public
Full restaurant/dining facilities:	Yes	No
Food suitable for vegetarians:	Yes	Yes
Bars:	1	1

Travel:
Car parking: At ground
Nearest station: Gloucester Central

Buses: Information: 01703-529090. Park & ride on Saturdays.

Tourist information: Gloucester TIC, St Michael's Tower, The Cross, GL1 1PD. 01452-421188. Fax: 01452-504273.

Road directions:

Ground on A417 (St Oswald's Road), just south of junction with A40. To north of city centre. 0.25 miles from Cathedral. From M5 junction 12, A38 then A430 towards city centre. From M5 junction 11, A40 then A417.

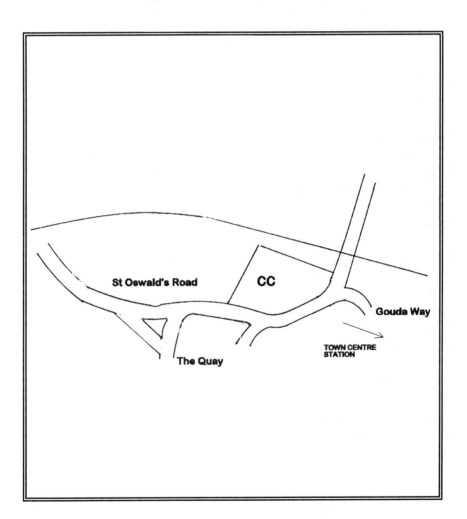

Signs of cricket: Cardiff, Portsmouth, Lytham (PDL)

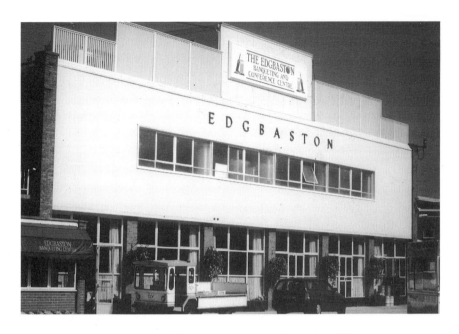

Banqueting and Conference Centre, Edgbaston (PDL)

Kwik Cricket - The Foster's Oval (RO)

54

Hampshire CCC

Club address: County Cricket Ground, Northlands Road, Southampton, Hants, SO15 2UE
Telephone: 01703-333788   **Fax:** 01703-330121
Ticket Office: As above
Other telephone numbers:
County Club (includes restaurant, gymnasium and squash): 01703-334393
Rapid Cricketline: 0891-567506
Grounds: Southampton - County Ground
　　　　　　　Basingstoke - Basingstoke & North Hants CC - May's Bounty
　　　　　　　Portsmouth - United Services CC

1997 Membership Subscriptions:

Full:	£76
Country:	£64
Junior:	£19
(Under 18)	
Students and 18-21:	£38
(Includes full-time students under 25 on 1/4/97)	
Country students and 18/21:	£33
Senior citizens:	£49
(Aged 60 on 1/4/97)	
Country (senior):	£42
Company (10 tickets):	£550

Life membership also available.
Parking: Season ticket   £44
(existing holders)

Reciprocal arrangements:
Free entry on Sundays for visiting junior members - all counties. Away matches: members normally have membership privileges at the opposing county's ground, after paying admission fee.

Ground admission reductions given for:

Senior citizens:	Yes
School students:	Yes
Up to age:	Under 18
Unemployed:	No
Students:	No

Supporters Club:
None

Corporate entertaining:
Hospitality boxes and marquees available. Also have Executive Club: £300 plus VAT for one year, £550 plus VAT for two years, £800 plus VAT for three years. Contact Marketing Department for details.

Visually impaired people:
No reduced admission. Guide dogs allowed.

The County Ground, Southampton (RO)

Temporary stand, United Services Ground, Portsmouth (PL)

Hampshire CCC
County Ground: Southampton

Description of ground: Hampshire first played a Championship game at the County Ground in 1885, a pleasant suburban setting outside the city centre. Developments have included the indoor cricket school, County Club (squash and gym) in 1982 and Philip Mead Stand in 1987. Ground includes practice pitches, tennis courts and bowls.

Address: Northlands Road, Southampton, Hants, SO15 2UE
Telephone: 01703-333788   **Capacity:** 5,000

General facilities:
Club shop: Yes
Club museum: Yes
Cricket coaching facilities: Yes
Cricket nets: Yes - professionals only in summer. Clubs in winter.
Other sporting or recreational facilities on the ground: Squash, gym, indoor nets (October - April)
Facilities for hire or wider community use at the ground: Restaurant and some conference facilities.

Facilities and access for people with disabilities:
Wheelchair access to the ground: Yes
Designated car parking available inside the ground: Yes
Good viewing areas inside the ground for people using wheelchairs: Yes
Designated viewing areas: Yes
Ramps to provide easy access to bars and refreshment outlets: No

Food & drink:

	Members	General Public
Full restaurant/dining facilities:	Yes	Yes
Food suitable for vegetarians:	Yes	Yes
Bars:	2	1

Travel:
Car parking: Ticket holders only at ground. Limited street parking.

Nearest station:
Southampton Central

58

handwritten at top:
47 - 147 Hampshire ...
Southampton - Winchester
Eileen Beuchling 48 Southampton - Eastleigh
within to mile

Buses: 5,14B,16.
Information: 01703-224854
Tourist information: Southampton

TIC, 9, Civic Centre Rd, S014 7LP.
01703-221106.
Fax: 01703-631437.

Road directions:

Take A33 (The Avenue) towards Southampton city centre. Approx 1.5 miles north of city centre, turn right into Northlands Road. Ground is signposted. Northlands Road is first turning on right at end of Southampton Common on right-hand side. AA yellow signs from M3/A33 to Northlands Road.

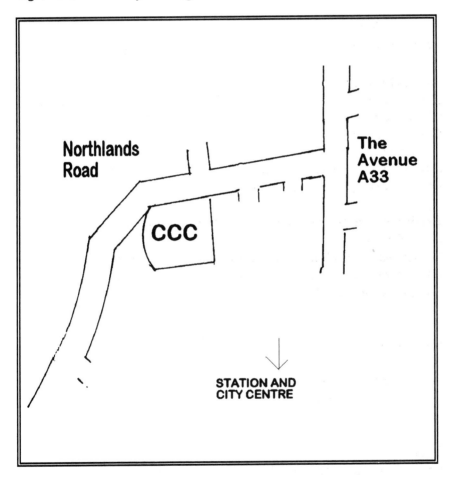

Northlands Road

The Avenue A33

CCC

STATION AND
CITY CENTRE

Hampshire CCC
Basingstoke & North Hants CC

Description of ground: Attractive historic club ground, with period pavilion. First used for cricket in 1855, Hampshire first played there in 1906. South of town centre.

Address: May's Bounty, Bounty Road, Basingstoke, Hampshire, RG21 2DR.
Telephone: 01256-473646   **Capacity:** 3,000

General facilities:
Club shop: Yes
Club museum: No
Cricket coaching facilities: No
Cricket nets: Yes - contact club
Other sporting or recreational

facilities on the ground: Squash, darts - contact club..
Facilities for hire or wider community use at the ground: No

Facilities and access for people with disabilities:
Wheelchair access to the ground: Yes
Designated car parking available inside the ground: Yes
Good viewing areas inside the ground for people using wheelchairs: Yes
Designated viewing areas: Yes
Ramps to provide easy access to bars and refreshment outlets: No

Food & drink:

	Members	General Public
Full restaurant/dining facilities:	No	No
Food suitable for vegetarians:	No	No
Bars:	1	1

Travel:
Car parking: Adjacent to ground. £3.50 per day. Street parking very restricted.
Nearest station: Basingstoke

Buses: 37, 38, 39, 55, 56, 76 from town bus centre.
Information: 01256-464501

Tourist information: Basingstoke TIC, Willis Museum, Old Town Hall, Market Place, RG21 7QD.

01256-817618.
Fax: 01256-51383.

Road directions:

M3 Junction 6. Turn left at roundabout onto ring road, and at next roundabout turn right into Hackwood Rd. Turn left into Southern Road, cross Victoria Street into Bounty Road - ground on left.

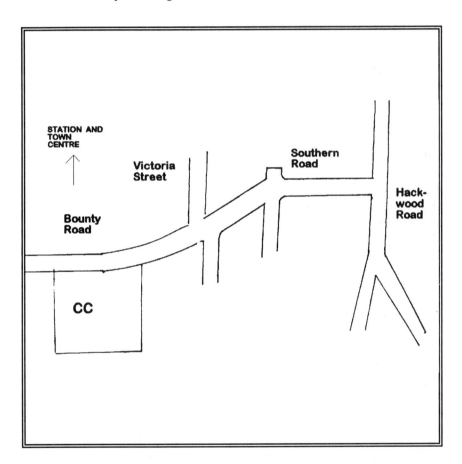

Hampshire CCC
Portsmouth - United Services CC

Description of ground: Well appointed ground, shared with US Portsmouth Rugby Club. Very near town centre, with Portsmouth University buildings on one side, and railway line on the other. Marquees and temporary stands provided for the County's annual visit.

Address: Burnaby Road, Portsmouth, Hampshire, PO1 2EJ
Telephone: 01705-830125   **Capacity:** 4,500

General facilities:
Club shop: Yes
Club museum: No
Cricket coaching facilities: No
Cricket nets: Yes
Other sporting or recreational

facilities on the ground: Rugby Union & Hockey
Facilities for hire or wider community use at the ground: No

Facilities and access for people with disabilities:
Wheelchair access to the ground: Yes
Designated car parking available inside the ground: Yes
Good viewing areas inside the ground for people using wheelchairs: Yes
Designated viewing areas: No
Ramps to provide easy access to bars and refreshment outlets: No

Food & drink:

	Members	General Public
Full restaurant/dining facilities:	Yes	No
Food suitable for vegetarians:	Yes	No
Bars:	2	1

Travel:
Road restrictions on match days: No parking in Burnaby Rd.
Car parking: Opposite ground entrance £3.50 per day. Some street parking a few minutes walk from ground. Also local car parks.
Nearest station: Portsmouth & Southsea.

Buses: Information: 01705-650967
Tourist information:
Portsmouth TIC, The Hard,
Portsmouth PO1 3QJ.
01705-826722.
Fax: 01705-822693.

Road directions:

M275 into city centre, then A3 follow signs for Portsea or ferries. AA signs for county cricket. Burnaby Road is right turn off Cambridge Road.

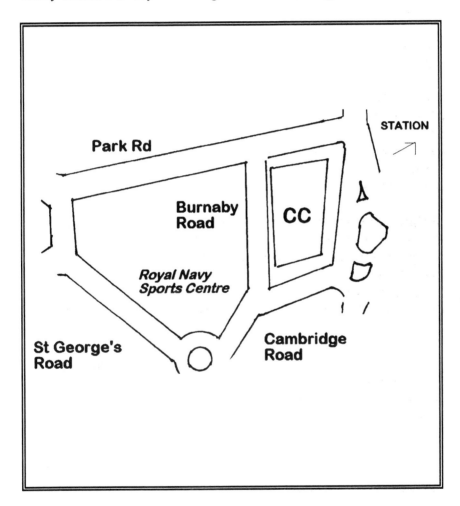

Kent CCC

Club address: St Lawrence Ground, Old Dover Road, Canterbury, Kent, CT1 3NZ
Telephone: 01227-456886 **Fax:** 01227-762168
Ticket Office: As above.
Other telephone numbers:
Rapid Cricketline: 0891-567507
Ames-Levett Sports Centre: 01227-784996. Fax: 01227-453130
Grounds: Canterbury - County Ground
Maidstone - The Mote CC - Mote Park
Tunbridge Wells - Tunbridge Wells CC - Nevill Ground

1997 Membership Subscriptions:

Member, friend and car:	£135
Member, friend and car: (country)	£91
Member and friend:	£98
Member and friend (country):	£65
Member and car:	£98
Member and car (country):	£65
Single:	£59
Single (country):	£40
Junior (under 18):	£18
Junior (under 18 - country):	£12
Student (18 - 23):	£32
Student (18-23, country):	£27
Harris Room: (Ordinary/Corporate)	£400
Harris Room: (Single)	£235

Senior citizens: Over 65, £12 off full membership and £8 off country membership.
Juniors (7-14): Free membership of Invicta FM Juniors Club
Life membership also available.
Country membership: Living outside Kent, E.Sussex, Surrey, Essex, Middlesex and Greater London.

Reciprocal arrangements:
Junior Invicta Club members: Free admission at away Championship and Sunday League games

Ground admission reductions given for:

Senior citizens:	Yes
School students:	Yes
Up to age:	18
Unemployed:	No
Students:	No

Supporters Club:
C/o Kent CCC as above.

Corporate hospitality:
Function room and other entertainment facilities at Ames-Levett Sports Centre (Canterbury).

Marquees, boxes, conference and banqueting facilities available at matches. Contact the Marketing Manager for details. Facilities also available for meetings, training days, exhibitions etc.

Visually impaired people:
Free entry, also for helper. Guide dogs allowed. Give club advance warning as soon as possible.

Sunday cricket at Canterbury (PDL)

Festival cricket at Tunbridge Wells (PDL)

65

Kent CCC
St Lawrence Ground: Canterbury

Description of ground: Canterbury weeks date from the great days of Felix, Pilch and Alfred Mynn (1834 - 1850), and the August festival is a traditional annual pleasure. The St Lawrence Ground has a treein the playing area and spectators watch play from their cars and the pavilion and modern buildings blend harmoniously with the general rural scene.

Address: St Lawrence Ground, Old Dover Road, Canterbury, CT1 3NZ
Telephone: 01227-456886   **Capacity:** 12,000

General facilities:

Club shop: Yes

Club museum: No

Cricket coaching facilities: Yes - contact club for details

Cricket nets: Yes

Other sporting or recreational facilities on the ground: Yes - sports centre 01227-784996

Facilities for hire or wider community use at the ground: Yes

Facilities and access for people with disabilities:

Wheelchair access to the ground: Yes
Designated car parking available inside the ground: Yes
Good viewing areas inside the ground for people using wheelchairs: Yes
Designated viewing areas: Yes
Ramps to provide easy access to bars and refreshment outlets: Yes

Food & drink:

	Members	General Public
Full restaurant/dining facilities:	Yes	Yes
Food suitable for vegetarians:	Yes	Yes
Bars:	3	3

Travel:

Car parking: Large car park at ground. £6.50. Also some street parking.

Nearest station: Canterbury East
Buses: Information: 01227-472082.

Kent Council transport information: 0800-696996
Special transport arrangements on match days: 17 bus from Folkestone

Tourist information: Canterbury TIC, 34, St Margaret's St, CT1 2TG.
01227-766567.
Fax: 01227-459840

Road directions:

From M2: take A2. Pass first Canterbury turn off. Take turn off for Bridge. Turn right, then fork right and follow signs for Canterbury (A290). This becomes Old Dover Road - ground on left.
From City Centre, take Old Dover Road turn off at roundabout by bus station, and this leads to the ground.

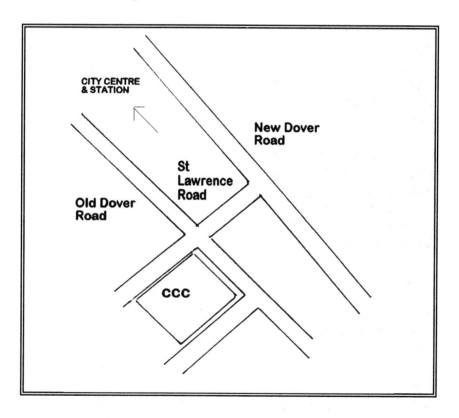

Kent CCC
Maidstone - The Mote Cricket Club

Description of ground: Very attractive setting, with excellent views of Kent countryside. Club ground based in public park. Just outside town centre. First used by Kent in the 1850s, and regularly from 1870.

Address: Mote Park, Willow Way, Maidstone, Kent.
Telephone: 01622-754159. For Kent matches: 01622-754545
Capacity: 8,000

General facilities:
Club shop: Yes
Club museum: No
Cricket coaching facilities: Yes
Cricket nets: Yes - contact the club
Other sporting or recreational facilities on the ground: The Mote Squash Club: 01622-676977.
Rugby Union (Maidstone FC)
Facilities for hire or wider community use at the ground: No
Other sporting recreational / leisure activities: Other leisure facilities in Mote Park.

Facilities and access for people with disabilities:
Wheelchair access to the ground: Yes
Designated car parking available inside the ground: Yes
Good viewing areas inside the ground for people using wheelchairs: Yes
Designated viewing areas: Yes
Ramps to provide easy access to bars and refreshment outlets: Yes

Food & drink:

	Members	General Public
Full restaurant/dining facilities:	Yes	No
Food suitable for vegetarians:	Yes	Yes
Bars:	1	1

Travel:
Car parking: Some at ground £6.50. Street parking very restricted.
Nearest station: Maidstone East

or Maidstone West
Buses: Near bus station. 85 from High Street and Chequers Centre. Kent Council transport information: 0800-696996

Tourist information: Maidstone TIC, The Gatehouse, Palace Gardens, Mill Street, ME15 6YE. 01622-602169
Fax: 01622-673581.

Road directions:

From town centre, take A20 (Ashford Rd). Turn right into Square Hill, and continue into Square Hill Road. At roundabout, turn left into Mote Avenue, and follow road round into Willow Way. Ground on left.

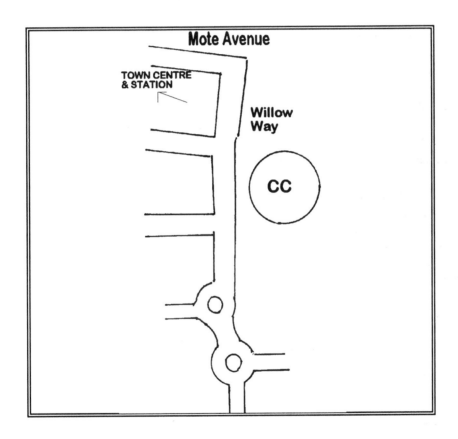

Kent CCC
Tunbridge Wells Cricket Club

Description of ground: Very attractive club ground with modern pavilion and stand, with marquees for the lucky ones and the general pleasure of everyone else. Ideal for festival week. First used by Kent in 1901. In 1913 the Pavilion was burnt down by suffragettes.

Address: Nevill Cricket Ground, Nevill Gate, Warwick Park, TN2 5ES
Telephone: 01892-520846   **Capacity:** 5,500

General facilities:

Club shop: Yes

Club museum: No

Cricket coaching facilities: Contact club

Cricket nets: Contact club

Other sporting or recreational facilities on the ground: No

Facilities for hire or wider community use at the ground: No

Other sporting recreational / leisure activities: Tennis next door to ground.

Facilities and access for people with disabilities:
Wheelchair access to the ground: Yes
Designated car parking available inside the ground: Yes
Good viewing areas inside the ground for people using wheelchairs: Yes
Designated viewing areas: Yes
Ramps to provide easy access to bars and refreshment outlets: Yes

Food & drink:

	Members	General Public
Full restaurant/dining facilities:	Yes	Yes
Food suitable for vegetarians:	Yes	Yes
Bars:	1	1

Travel:
Road restrictions on match days: No parking in roads near ground.
Car parking: Some at ground.

£6.50. Park and ride scheme.
Nearest station: Tunbridge Wells
Buses: Stop on Forest Rd. Kent

Council transport information:
0800-696996
Special transport arrangements on match days: Park and ride. Signposted.

Tourist information:
Tunbridge Wells TIC, The Old Fish Market, The Pantiles, TN2 5TN.
01892-515675.
Fax: 01892-534660

Road directions:

From A21 take A264 (Pembury Rd) towards town centre. Turn left into Kingswood Rd, and then left into Bayhall Rd. Follow road round. This becomes Forest Road. Warwick Park is on right, and ground is after playing field on right hand side.

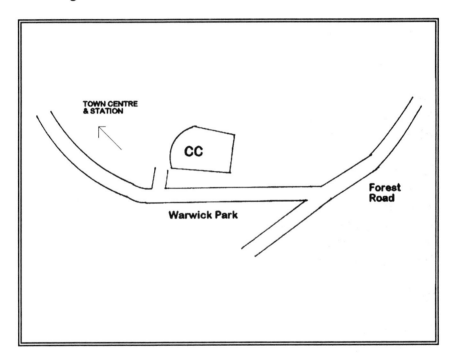

Lancashire CCC

Club address: Old Trafford, Warwick Road, Manchester, M16 0PX
Telephone: 0161-282-4000   **Fax:** 0161-282-4100
Ticket Office: 0161-282-4040
Other telephone numbers:
Conference & catering: 0161-282-4020. Fax: 0161-282-4030
Club shop: 0161-282-4050
Lancashire Cricket Board: 0161-282-4029. Fax: 0161-482-4100
Rapid Cricketline: 0891-567508
Grounds: Manchester - Old Trafford
          Blackpool - Blackpool CC - Stanley Park
          Liverpool - Liverpool CC
          Lytham - Lytham CC
          Southport - Southport and Birkdale CC

1997 Membership Subscriptions:

Full (22 and over):	£107
Full (65 and over):	£52.70
Full (18-21):	£36.50
Subscribers:	
Junior under 18:	£19.80
Member / Subscriber Child under 18 (children of members):	£9.90
Non employed & registered disabled:	£32.70
Country 30-50 miles:	
Aged 18 and over:	£84.70
Aged 65 and over:	£45
Non employed & registered disabled:	£27.50
Country over 50 miles:	
Aged 18 and over:	£70.70
Aged 65 and over:	£36.80
Non employed & registered disabled:	£21.80

(All above include joining fees)

Company (2 tickets):	£250
Company (extra tickets):	£104.50
Overseas:	£20.90

(Not including ground admission)
Life membership also available
Car Parking: Unreserved permit £38

Reciprocal arrangements:
Use of members facilities at away matches involving Lancashire CCC. Also arrangement with the WACA, Perth, Australia.

Ground admission reductions given for:

Senior citizens:	Yes
School students:	Yes
Up to age:	16
Unemployed:	No
Students:	No

Other: Family ticket available for Sunday League matches

Supporters Club:
Mr C Blakely
Red Rose Travel Club
8 Winsford Grove,Ladybridge
Bolton, Lancashire, BL3 4QD

Corporate facilities:
Old Trafford has facilities for dinners, conferences, weddings, exhibitions, dinner dances, etc. Executive suites and boxes also available for matches. The County Restaurant is open from midday to 3.00 pm Monday to Friday, and before Manchester United homes matches. Further information from Conference and Catering office, as above.

Visually impaired people:
Free entry, also for helper. No guide dogs allowed.

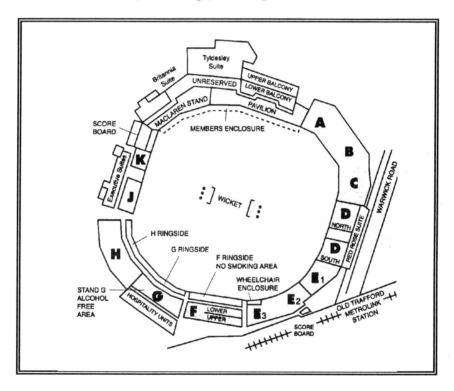

Old Trafford plan - courtesy Lancashire CCC

The Pavilion, Old Trafford (PDL)

Ladies Pavilion, Blackpool Cricket Club (PDL)

THE ULTIMATE TEST
ENGLAND V AUSTRALIA

ASHES 1997

3RD CORNHILL INSURANCE
TEST MATCH
AT OLD TRAFFORD JULY 3-7th
☎ TICKETS: 0161 - 282 - 4040 VISA

☎ HOSPITALITY: 0161 - 282 - 4020 MasterCard

Lancashire CCC
Old Trafford

Description of ground: One of the main Test match venues. Substantial modernisation has seen new stands and facilities built. Outside the centre of Manchester, but well served by public transport. Near Manchester United's Old Trafford. Look out for stands named after past Lancashire heroes, the Alcohol Free Stand, and visit the excellent museum. First used by Lancashire in 1865, and for a Test match in 1884.

Address: Old Trafford, Warwick Road, Manchester, M16 0PX.
Telephone: 0161-282-4000   **Capacity:** 21,000

General facilities:
Club shop: Yes
Club museum: Yes - match days only. Free admission.
Cricket coaching facilities: Yes - for schools and clubs. (Not on all match days)
Cricket nets: Indoor cricket school.

Other sporting or recreational facilities on the ground: Squash
Facilities for hire or wider community use at the ground: Conference, exhibition and banqueting facilities, for up to 450 people.

Facilities and access for people with disabilities:
Wheelchair access to the ground: Yes
Designated car parking available inside the ground: Yes
Good viewing areas inside the ground for people using wheelchairs: Yes
Designated viewing areas: Yes (By "F" enclosure and by pavilion)
Ramps to provide easy access to bars and refreshment outlets: Yes

Food & drink:

	Members	General Public
Full restaurant/dining facilities:	Yes	Yes
Food suitable for vegetarians:	Yes	Yes
Bars:	3	6

Additional food outlets and bars are provided during Test matches and one day internationals

Travel:

Car parking: £3 per day at ground. Limited street parking. Additional parking at Kings Road School, Stretford Sports Centre and Manchester United FC for major matches.
Nearest station: Old Trafford (Metrolink) Enquiries: 0161-205-2000.

Buses: 0161-228-7811. 115, 52 and 53 near ground, or any bus down Chester Road.
Tourist information: Manchester Visitor Centre, Town Hall Extension, Lloyd St, M60 2LA. 0161-234-3157/3158. Fax: 0161-236-9900.

Road directions:

From M63 junction 7, take A56 towards Manchester. Fork right onto A5067, Talbot Road, and ground is on right. From city centre, take A56 south, and fork left onto A5067. N.B. Ground is 0.25 miles from Manchester United ground - heavy traffic congestion at home matches.

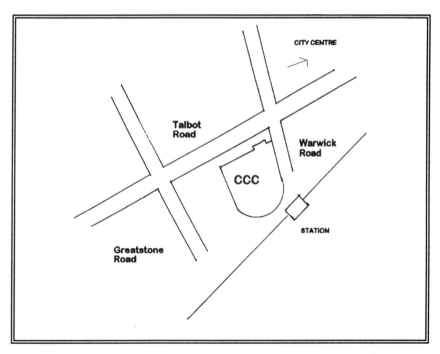

Lancashire CCC
Blackpool Cricket Club

Description of ground: Well appointed club ground situated in public park. Substantial pavilion and permanent seating. First used by Lancashire in 1904. Look out for the Ladies Pavilion - which houses a nursery during the week.

Address: Stanley Park, West Park Drive, Blackpool, Lancashire, FY3 9GQ
Telephone: 01253-393347   **Capacity:** 8,000

General facilities:
Club shop: Yes
Club museum: No
Cricket coaching facilities: Members only
Cricket nets: Members only
Facilities for hire or wider community use at the ground:
Used for junior & schools cricket
Other sporting recreational / leisure activities: Next door to athletics track. Sports centre and other facilities in Stanley Park. Rugby training at ground.

Facilities and access for people with disabilities:
Wheelchair access to the ground: Yes
Designated car parking available inside the ground: Yes - contact club
Good viewing areas inside the ground for people using wheelchairs: Yes
Designated viewing areas: Yes
Ramps to provide easy access to bars and refreshment outlets: Yes

Food & drink:

	Members	General Public
Full restaurant/dining facilities:	Yes	Yes
Food suitable for vegetarians:	Yes	Yes
Bars:	1	3

Travel:
Car parking: Some adjoining ground. £3 per day. Also in Stanley Park. Some street parking.

Nearest station: Blackpool North
Buses: 21,44b from Abington Street to Stanley Park gates.

Information: 01253-23931
Tourist information:
Blackpool TIC, 1, Clifton St,

FY1 1LY. 01253-21623.
Fax: 01253-26368

Road directions:
M55 take Junction 4. Take left hand lane for North Shore. Turn right into South Park Drive. At mini roundabout, turn left into West Park Drive. Drive along park, past sports centre. Ground on right.

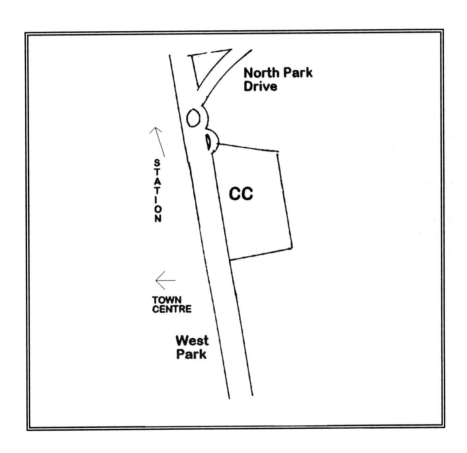

Lancashire CCC
Liverpool Cricket Club

Description of ground: Club ground in suburban area of Liverpool. Historic pavilion with fascinating old photos and paintings. First county match against Cambridge University in 1881.

Address: The Pavilion, Aigburth Road, Grassendale, Liverpool, L19 3QF
Telephone: 0151-427-2930.   **Capacity:** 8,000 (county matches)

General facilities:
Club shop: Yes
Club museum: No (but very interesting old pictures in pavilion)
Cricket coaching facilities: Yes
Cricket nets: Yes (summer only)
Other sporting or recreational facilities on the ground: Tennis, Football, Rugby Union, Bowls, Squash, Hockey.
Facilities for hire or wider community use at the ground: Function rooms
Other sporting recreational / leisure activities: Gymnasium

Facilities and access for people with disabilities:
Wheelchair access to the ground: Yes
Designated car parking available inside the ground: Yes
Good viewing areas inside the ground for people using wheelchairs: Yes
Designated viewing areas: Yes
Ramps to provide easy access to bars and refreshment outlets: Not needed

Food & drink:

	Members	General Public
Full restaurant/dining facilities:	Yes	No
Food suitable for vegetarians:	Yes	Yes
Bars:	2	1

Travel:
Road restrictions on match days: No parking near ground - roads coned off.

Car parking: On lower ground at end of Riversdale Rd. Also street parking.

Nearest station: Aigburth or Cressington. 0151-236-7676 *Buses:* 20, 26, 32, 82. Information: 0151-236-7676

Tourist information: Merseyside Welcome Centre, Clayton Sq Shopping Centre, L1 1QR. 0151-709-3631. Fax: 0151-708-0204

Road directions:
On A561 Aigburth Rd south of city centre, leading to Widnes and Runcorn. At junction with Riversdale Rd. Ground is signposted.

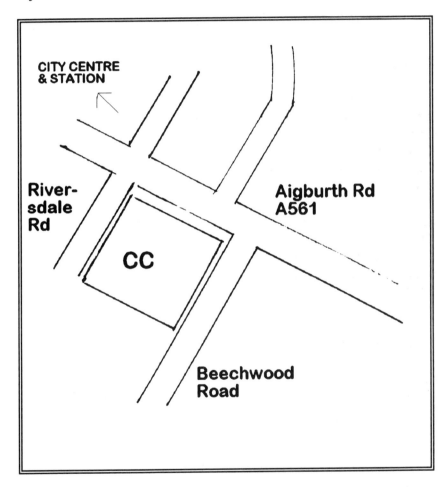

Lancashire CCC
Lytham Cricket Club

Description of ground: First used by Lancashire in 1985, the club was founded in 1855 by the Squire of Lytham, to provide cricket for his estate workers and local people. Prior to the first county match, had staged benefit games and second XI matches. Situated in Lytham town centre, fairly near the sea front.

Address: Church Road, Lytham, FY8 5DQ
Telephone: 01253-734137　　　　**Capacity:** 5,000

General facilities

Club shop: Yes
Club museum: No
Cricket coaching facilities: Yes - summer & part of winter. Members only
Cricket nets: Yes- summer & part of winter. Members only

Other sporting or recreational facilities on the ground: Tennis, Football and Hockey
Facilities for hire or wider community use at the ground: Function facilities and sports facilities

Facilities and access for people with disabilities

Wheelchair access to the ground: Yes
Designated car parking available inside the ground: Yes
Good viewing areas inside the ground for people using wheelchairs: Yes
Designated viewing areas: No
Ramps to provide easy access to bars and refreshment outlets: Yes

Food & drink:

	Members	General Public
Full restaurant/dining facilities:	Yes	No
Food suitable for vegetarians:	Yes	Yes
Bars:	2	2

Travel:

Car parking: At ground. Street parking available. Also YMCA ground 400 yards away.
Nearest station: Lytham
Buses: 11,11a, 193

Tourist information: Lytham St Ann'es TIC, 290, Clifton Drive South, FY8 1LH. 01253-725610. Fax: 01253-713754

Road directions:

M55 take junction 4. Take A5230 towards South Shore. Turn left at traffic lights into Common Edge Road B5261, signposted Lytham St Anne's. Stay on this road, which becomes Church Road, and ground on left.

Alternative: Take A584 along sea front, turn left into Woodville Terrace, and ground at end of road.

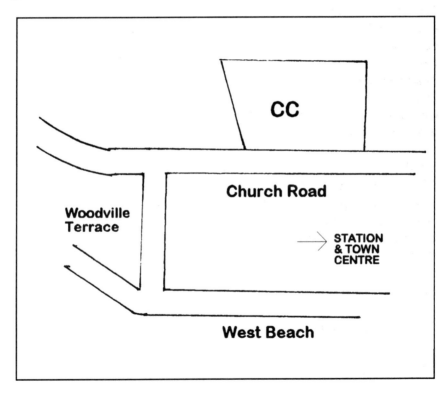

Lancashire CCC
Southport & Birkdale Cricket Club

Description of ground: Pleasant club ground with modern pavilion. Next to Liverpool railway line. Just south of town centre, fairly near the beach. First county match against Worcestershire in 1959.

Address: The Pavilion, Trafalgar Rd, Birkdale, Southport, PR8 2HF
Telephone: 01704-569951   **Capacity:** 5,000

General facilities
Club shop: Yes
Club museum: No
Cricket coaching facilities: Yes - summer & winter. Members and recognised clubs.
Cricket nets: Yes

Other sporting or recreational facilities on the ground: Tennis, Squash, Racketball and Hockey
Facilities for hire or wider community use at the ground: Conference and function facilities

Facilities and access for people with disabilities
Wheelchair access to the ground: Yes
Designated car parking available inside the ground: Yes
Good viewing areas inside the ground for people using wheelchairs: Yes
Designated viewing areas: Yes
Ramps to provide easy access to bars and refreshment outlets: Yes

Food & drink:

	Members	General Public
Full restaurant/dining facilities:	Yes	Yes
Food suitable for vegetarians:	Yes	No
Bars:	2	2

Travel:
Car parking: None at ground. Street parking restricted. Use Royal Birkdale Golf Club.
Nearest station: Southport. Local service: Birkdale or Hillside
Buses: 5 from town centre. Stop on Grosvenor Rd.
Information: 0151-236-7676

Tourist information: Southport   01704-533333
TIC, 112 Lord St PR8 1NY.

Road directions:

Take A565 south from town centre. Turn left into Grosvenor Road, and right into Trafalgar Rd, and ground is on left. Coming from south, use A565, turn right into Grosvenor Rd, then as above. Parking at Royal Birkdale Golf Club.

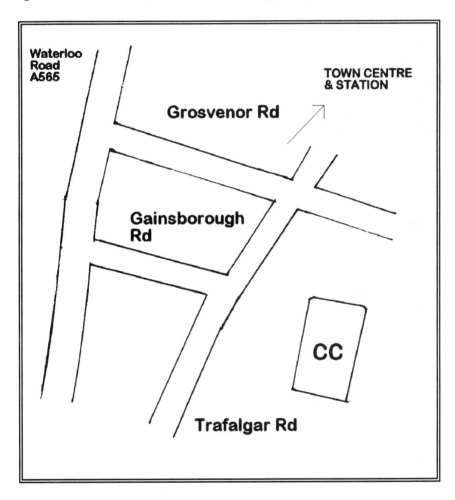

Leicestershire CCC

Club address: County Ground, Grace Road, Leicester, LE2 8AD
Telephone: 0116-283-2128 or 0116-283-1880   **Fax:** 0116-244-0363
Ticket Office: As above
Other telephone numbers:
Indoor cricket school: As above
Rapid Cricketline: 0891-567509
Grounds: Leicester - County Ground

1997 Membership Subscriptions:

Full: *	£30
Junior (13-18): *	£22
Charlie Fox Junior:	£10
(under 13):	
Senior citizen: *	£25
Gold: *	£65

Gold Junior (parents must have Gold membership): (Under 13) Free
Gold Junior (parents must have Gold membership): (13-18) £5
Company patron: £195

* New member introduction fee of £5 payable.

Three year and life membership also available.

Reciprocal arrangements:
Use of members' areas at away grounds when Leicestershire is playing away, after payment of ground admission fee.

Ground admission reductions given for:

Senior citizens:	Yes
School students:	Yes
Up to age:	18
Unemployed:	No
Students:	No

Supporters Club:
Mr D Hickling , Friends of Grace Road, 11, Sherborne Avenue, Wigston Magna, Leicester LE18 2GP

Corporate entertaining:
Conference facilities, suites for wedding receptions, dinners etc. Suites and boxes available for matches. Contact Marketing Department for details.

Visually impaired people:
Sometimes two for one price reduction. Guide dogs allowed. Contact club in advance.

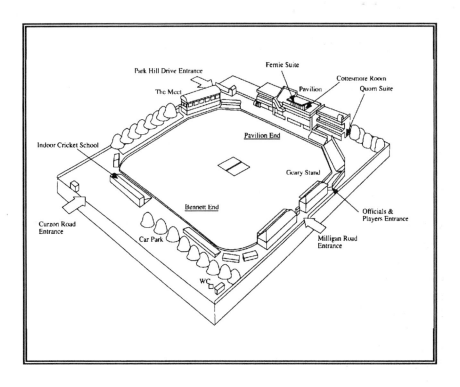

Grace Road plan - courtesy Leicestershire CCC

A damp day at Leicester (PDL)

Leicestershire CCC
County Ground: Leicester

Description of ground: Currently the only ground used by 1996 County Champions Leicestershire. Compact modern ground. Used by Leicestershire from 1884 to 1900, and then again after the second world war. Many improvements added in recent years. Outside city centre.

Address: County Ground, Grace Road, Leicester, LE2 8AD
Telephone: 0116-283-2128 or 0113-283-1880   **Capacity:** 6,500

General facilities:
Club shop: Yes
Club museum: Yes
Cricket coaching facilities: Yes
Cricket nets: Yes - all year round
Other sporting or recreational
facilities on the ground: No
Facilities for hire or wider community use at the ground: Yes. Rooms for functions, conferences, meetings etc.

Facilities and access for people with disabilities:
Wheelchair access to the ground: Yes
Designated car parking available inside the ground: Yes
Good viewing areas inside the ground for people using wheelchairs: Yes
Designated viewing areas: No
Ramps to provide easy access to bars and refreshment outlets: For some, others have small steps, and stewards will assist.

Food & drink:

	Members	General Public
Full restaurant/dining facilities:	Yes	No
Food suitable for vegetarians:	Yes	Yes
Bars:	4	2

Travel:
Road restrictions on match days: No parking in streets immediately around ground.

Car parking: Car park at ground, and street parking.
Nearest station: Leicester

Buses: 26, 37,37a, 38, 38a, 47, 48, 48a, 68, 73,76.
Information: 0116-251-1411
Tourist information: Leicester TIC,

7/9 Every Street, Town Hall Sq, LE1 6AG. 0116-265-0555
Fax: 0116-255-5726

Road directions:

From M1 junction 21, take A563 towards city centre. Turn left onto A426 (Luterworth Rd), which becomes Aylestone Rd. After 1 mile, turn right into Grace Road. Ground is south of city centre. From city centre, take A426 from inner ring road, turn left into Grace Road. Not always easy to find. Members entrance at Grace Road end. Hawkesbury Road entrance leads to car park and then playing area.

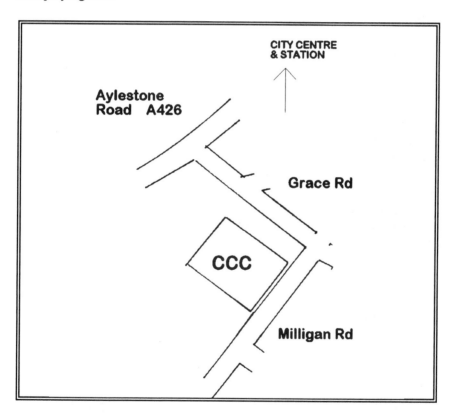

Middlesex CCC

Club address: Lords Cricket Ground, St Johns Wood Road, London, NW8 8QN
Telephone: 0171-289-1300　　　　**Fax:** 0171-289-5831
Ticket Office: As above
Other telephone numbers:
Membership: 0171-286-5453
Shop: 0171-286-1310
Cricket and Squash Centre (Finchley): 0181-346-8020
Grounds: Lords
　　　　　Uxbridge - Uxbridge CC

1997 Membership Subscriptions:
Gentleman members:

Full (18-64): *	£75
Country: *	£43
Junior (Aged 8 -17):	£21
Junior Colts:	£11
Student:	£27

(for existing junior members on becoming 18 & in full-time education)

Senior citizen (65 & over):	£43
Middlesex/MCC:	£22

(MCC members only)

Lady members:

Full (18-59): *	£53
Senior citizen (60 & over):	£32
Country: *	£32
Executive Club:	£200

* New member's £25 entrance fee

Country membership is 50 miles from Lords.

Abroad:	£22

Reductions given on most rates for payment by direct debit.

Life membership also available.

N.B. Lady members are not allowed into the Pavilion at Lords

Reciprocal arrangements:
After paying the ground admission fee, access to the Pavilion and Members' Enclosures at Middlesex CCC away matches

Ground admission reductions given for:

Senior citizens: (over 65):	Yes
School students:	Yes
Up to age:	16
Unemployed:	No
Students:	No

Supporters Club:
The Seaxe Club, c/o Middlesex CCC, Lord's, St John's Wood Road, NW8 8QN
Membership: Jane Saxton in the Seaxe Box in the Tavern Stand on Middlesex match days.
Travel:
Steve Baldwin 0956-439807 and Anne Masters: 0956-364919.

Tea interval, Uxbridge (RO)

Inspecting the wicket, Uxbridge (RO)

Middlesex CCC
Uxbridge Cricket Club

Description of ground: One of the oldest clubs, founded in 1798. Well maintained ground with modern pavilion. First used by Middlesex in 1980, two local streets are named after Mike Gatting and Mike Brearley. Next door to the local Rugby Club, the local Ski Slope is also near the ground.

Address: Gatting Way, Park Road, Uxbridge
Telephone: 01895-237571   **Capacity:** 3,500

General facilities:
Club shop: Yes
Club museum: No
Cricket coaching facilities: Contact club
Cricket nets: Contact club
Other sporting or recreational facilities by the ground: Squash, tennis, Rugby Union, ski slope.
Facilities for hire or wider community use at the ground: Contact club

Facilities and access for people with disabilities:
Wheelchair access to the ground: Yes
Designated car parking available inside the ground: Yes
Good viewing areas inside the ground for people using wheelchairs: Yes
Designated viewing areas: No
Ramps to provide easy access to bars and refreshment outlets: Not necessary

Food & drink:

	Members	General Public
Full restaurant/dining facilities:	Yes	Yes
Food suitable for vegetarians:	Yes	Yes
Bars:	1	1

Travel:
Car parking: At ground.
Nearest station: Uxbridge

(London Underground)
Information: 0171-222-1234

Buses: U1, U2, U10. Bus station by underground station.
Information: 0171-222-1234

Special transport arrangements on match days: Occasionally provided.

Road directions:
From A40, take B483(Park Road) south towards Uxbridge, and ground is on left. This A40 junction is the last one before the start of the M40, leaving London. AA signs used when Middlesex playing at Uxbridge.

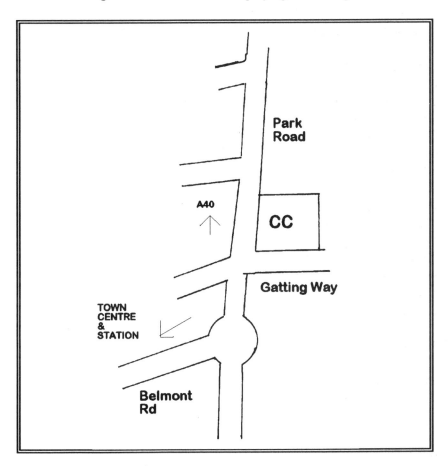

Northamptonshire CCC

Club address: County Cricket Ground, Wantage Road, Northampton, NN1 4TJ
Telephone: 01604-32917   **Fax:** 01604-232855
Ticket Office: As above
Other telephone numbers:
Rapid Cricketline: 0891-567511
Restaurant bookings for match days: Trio Caterers 01604-30376
Grounds: County Ground - Northampton
           Luton - Luton Town CC - Wardown Park
           Milton Keynes - Campbell Park

1997 Membership Subscriptions:
Member: £68
Tudor Junior: (under 16) £15
Students: (16 and over, in full-time education): £27
Senior citizens: (65 & over): £48
Family: £145
(2 ordinary & 2 student tickets)
Vice President: £145
Business House: £310 + VAT
Executive Club (Individual): £260 + VAT
Executive Club (with guest): £325 + VAT

Reciprocal arrangements:
Use of members' facilities at away matches

Ground admission reductions given for:

Senior citizens:	Yes
School students:	Yes
Up to age:	16
Unemployed:	No
Students:	Yes

Supporters Club:
Mr B. Darker, 6, Gloucester Close, Northampton, NN4 8PW. 01604-761055.

Corporate entertaining:
Conference, dinner & restaurant facilities at ground. Contact club for details of corporate facilities at matches.

Visually impaired people:
No reduced admission. Guide dogs allowed.

The County Ground, Northampton (PDL)

Campbell Park, Milton Keynes (PDL)

Northamptonshire CCC
Northampton: County Ground

Description of ground: Modern pavilion and stand with other smaller stands. Formerly shared with Northampton Town football team - but most signs of the football ground-share are now gone. Friendly atmosphere.

Address: County Cricket Ground, Wantage Road, Northampton, NN1 4TJ
Telephone: 01604-32917   **Capacity:** 4,500

General facilities
Club shop: Yes
Club museum: No
Cricket coaching facilities: Yes - winter only.
Cricket nets: Yes - winter only
Other sporting or recreational
facilities on the ground: No
Facilities for hire or wider community use at the ground: Conference, dinner and restaurant facilities.

Facilities and access for people with disabilities
Wheelchair access to the ground: Yes
Designated car parking available inside the ground: Yes
Good viewing areas inside the ground for people using wheelchairs: Yes
Designated viewing areas: Yes
Ramps to provide easy access to bars and refreshment outlets: Yes

Food & drink:

	Members	General Public
Full restaurant/dining facilities:	Yes	Yes
Food suitable for vegetarians:	Yes	Yes
Bars:	3	3

Travel:
Car parking: Some at ground £3. Also street parking.
Nearest station: Northampton.

Buses: 1, 51.
Information: 01604-20077

96

Tourist information:
Northampton Visitor Centre, Mr
Grant's House, 10, St Giles Sq,

NN1 1DA.   01604-22677.
Fax: 01604-604180.

Road directions:

Ground is north east of town centre. From A45, at junction with A428 and
A5095, take A5095 (Rushmere Rd). Turn left onto Wellingborough Rd
(A4500), and Wantage Rd is first on right. From town centre, take
Wellingborough Rd (A4500), then as above.

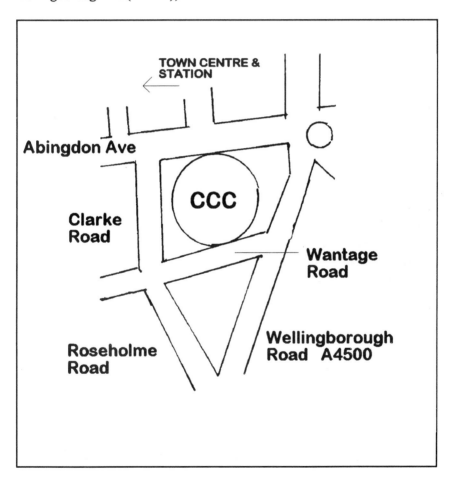

Northamptonshire CCC
Luton Town CC

Description of ground: Compact club ground with modern pavilion and scoreboard. Also used by Bedfordshire for Minor Counties cricket. Next door to the local museum, which is worth a visit during the lunch interval. There is another cricket ground in the park, adjoining this ground. North of town centre.

Address: Wardown Park, Old Bedford Road, Luton, Bedfordshire
Telephone: 01582-27855   **Capacity:** 5,000

General facilities:
Club shop: Yes
Club museum: No
Cricket coaching facilities: No
Cricket nets: No
Other sporting or recreational facilities on the ground: Hockey

Facilities for hire or wider community use at the ground: No
Other sporting recreational / leisure activities: Football, cricket & other leisure activites in park.

Facilities and access for people with disabilities:
Wheelchair access to the ground: Yes
Designated car parking available inside the ground: No
Good viewing areas inside the ground for people using wheelchairs: Yes
Designated viewing areas: Yes
Ramps to provide easy access to bars and refreshment outlets: No

Food & drink:

	Members	General Public
Full restaurant/dining facilities:	No	No
Food suitable for vegetarians:	Yes	Yes
Bars:	1	1

Travel:
Car parking: £2, in Wardown Park
Nearest station: Luton
Buses: 24 (by library), 25, 26 - stop
on Old Bedford Road.
Information: 0345-788788.
Green Line 757.

Tourist information: Luton TIC, The Bus Station, Bute Street, LU1 2EY. 01582-401579. Fax: 01582-487886

Road directions:

From M1 junction 11 take A505 towards town centre. Pass first sign for Bedford A6, but after entering one way system, follow signs for Bedford A6. At roundabout by park, turn right, and right again at traffic lights into Old Bedford Road.

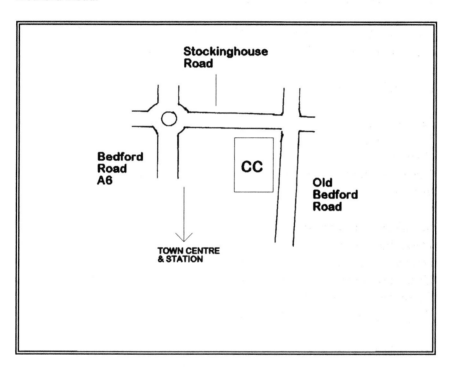

Northamptonshire CCC
Milton Keynes - Campbell Park

Description of ground: Stunning new ground. Banked grass slopes form good spectator viewing areas. Very impressive new pavilion, with excellent detailed architecture. Do not miss the weather vane, door decorations, and the sculpture behind the pavilion.

Address: Campbell Park, Silbury Boulevard, Milton Keynes
Telephone: 01908-694820   **Capacity:** 5,000 approx

General facilities
Club shop: Yes
Club museum: No
Cricket coaching facilities: No
Cricket nets: No
Other sporting or recreational

facilities on the ground: No
Facilities for hire or wider community use at the ground:
Contact Milton Keynes Parks Trust
01908-233600

Facilities and access for people with disabilities
Wheelchair access to the ground: Yes
Designated car parking available inside the ground: Yes
Good viewing areas inside the ground for people using wheelchairs: Yes
Designated viewing areas: No
Ramps to provide easy access to bars and refreshment outlets: Yes

Food & drink:

	Members	General Public
Full dining facilities:	Yes	No
Food suitable for vegetarians:	No	No
Bars:	1	1

Travel:
Car parking: Limited at ground. In park and some street parking.
Nearest station: Milton Keynes Central

Buses: 1, 17, 1E, 90, 19E all stop near ground.
Information: 0345-382000.

100

Tourist information: Milton Keynes TIC, 411, Secklow Gate East, The Food Hall, MK9 3NE.

01908-232525.
Fax: 01908-235050.

Road directions:
From M1 junction 14, take A509 (H5 Portway) towards city centre. Turn left at roundabout into North Overgate, and ground is straight ahead, over Cricket Green Roundabout. Campbell Park is well signposted.

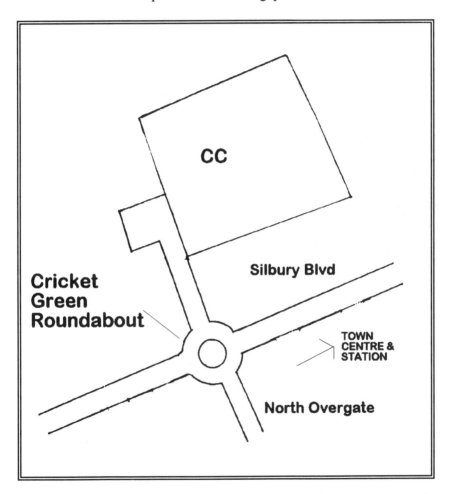

Nottinghamshire CCC

Club address: Trent Bridge, Bridgford Road, Nottingham, NG2 6AG
Telephone: 0115-982-1525   **Fax:** 0115-945-5730
Ticket Office: 0115-981-7005
Other telephone numbers:
Rapid Cricketline: 0891-567512
Scores & prospects for play: 0115-982-2753
Trent Bridge Banqueting: 0115-945-5321. Fax: 0115-981-9918
Grounds: Nottingham - Trent Bridge
         Worksop - Worksop Town CC

1997 Membership Subscriptions:
Ordinary:

Adult:	£60
Husband & wife / Member & Partner:	£90
Country:	£50
Country (Husband & wife / Member & Partner):	£75
Young Persons:	£15
(Under 21 on 1/4/97 and students)	
Junior (under 18):	£10
Senior citizen:	£40
Senior citizen: (Husband & wife / Member & Partner):	£60
Company (minimum 5 tickets):	£240
Additional tickets:	£50

Patron:
(Includes all Nat West Trophy & Benson & Hedges matches; and Cornhill Insurance test match if available).

Adult:	£160
Husband & wife / Member &	
Partner:	£285
Country:	£150
Country: (Husband & wife / Member & Partner):	£265
Young Persons:	£95
(Under 21 on 1/4/97 and students)	
Junior (under 18):	£70
Senior citizen:	£125
Senior citizen: (Husband & wife / Member & Partner):	£225
Company (minimum 5 tickets):	£740
Additional tickets:	£50
" " (Patrons)	£160
Taverners:	£18
(Admission to Taverners' Club only, does not include ground admission)	

A joining fee per category is payable by all new members except young persons and juniors.

Country: Living outside Nottinghamshire

Life membership also available - different rates according to age. Car Parking permits available for weekends & bank holidays. Also for disabled for all match days.

Reciprocal arrangements:
Subject to availability, admission, after paying ground admission, to members' facilities at other grounds when Nottinghamshire CCC is playing away. *Junior members:* Free admission to away matches.

Ground admission reductions given for:

Senior citizens:	Yes
School students:	Yes
Up to age:	18

Unemployed:	Yes
Students:	Yes

Supporters Club:
Mr W Gray, Notts CCSA, 85 Ingram Road, Bullwell, Nottingham NG6 9GP

Corporate entertaining:
Conference and banqueting rooms available for meals, buffets, meetings and dinner dances. Phone Trent Bridge Banqueting for further details.

Visually impaired people:
Reduced admission - not for helpers. Guide dogs allowed.

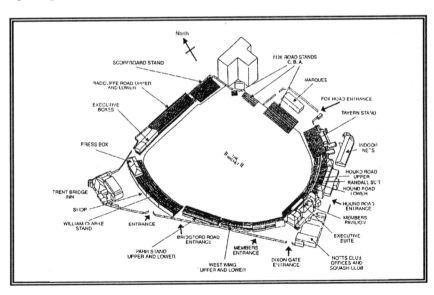

Trent Bridge Plan - courtesy of Nottinghamshire CCC

Nottinghamshire CCC
Trent Bridge

Description of ground: Modernised Test match ground, next door to Nottingham Forest Football Club. First used for cricket in the 1830s. Block of flats in the corner overshadows the scoreboard. Just outside the city centre, across the River Trent.

Address: Trent Bridge, Bridgford Road, Nottingham, NG2 6AG
Telephone: 0115-982-1525   **Capacity:** 11,750

General facilities:
Club shop: Yes
Club museum: Yes
Cricket coaching facilities: All year round.
Cricket nets: Yes. All year round
Other sporting or recreational facilities on the ground: Squash club
Facilities for hire or wider community use at the ground: Banqueting and conference facilities.

Facilities and access for people with disabilities:
Wheelchair access to the ground: Yes
Designated car parking available inside the ground: Yes
Good viewing areas inside the ground for people using wheelchairs: Yes
Designated viewing areas: Yes
Ramps to provide easy access to bars and refreshment outlets: Yes

Food & drink:

	Members	General Public
Full restaurant/dining facilities:	Yes	Yes
Food suitable for vegetarians:	Yes	Yes
Bars:	1	1

Travel:
Car parking: £4 at Nottingham Forest FC. Street parking restricted.
Nearest station: Nottingham

Buses: 1,2a, 10, 12, 29a, 71, 90.
Information: 0115-950-3665

Tourist information: Nottingham   0115-947-0661.
TIC 1-4 Smithy Row NG1 2BY.   Fax: 0115-915-5323

Road directions:

Near junction of A52 and A60, across Trent Bridge from city centre. Well signposted. Junction 25 from M1.

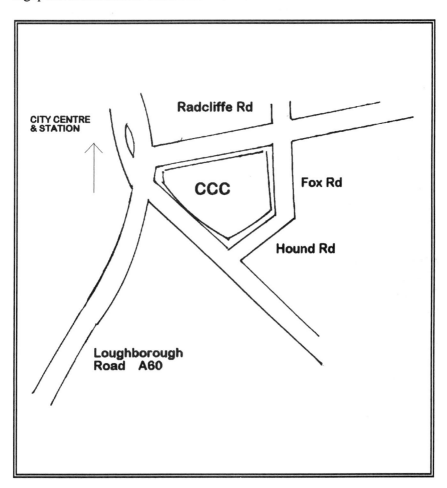

Nottinghamshire CCC
Worksop Town CC

Description of ground: Club ground with modern pavilion. Next to a caravan park. In town centre. First used by Nottinghamshire for county cricket in 1921, and currently the only ground used by the County outside Trent Bridge. Temporary seating and marquees are installed for county matches.

Address: Central Avenue, Worksop, Nottinghamshire
Telephone: 01909-472681   **Capacity:** 7,000

General facilities:
Club shop: Yes
Club museum: No
Cricket coaching facilities: No
Cricket nets: Contact club
Other sporting or recreational facilities on the ground: Squash club & bowls
Facilities for hire or wider community use at the ground: No

Facilities and access for people with disabilities:
Wheelchair access to the ground: Yes
Designated car parking available inside the ground: No
Good viewing areas inside the ground for people using wheelchairs: Yes
Designated viewing areas: No
Ramps to provide easy access to bars and refreshment outlets: Yes

Food & drink:

	Members	General Public
Full restaurant/dining facilities:	No	No
Food suitable for vegetarians:	Yes	Yes
Bars:	1	1

Travel:
Car parking: At ground. Members free, public £4. Also local car parks and street parking.
Nearest station: Worksop

Buses: Bus station very close to ground.
Information: 01777-710550

Tourist information: Worksop TIC, Worksop Library, Memorial Avenue S80 2BP. 01909- 501148. Fax: 01909-501611.

Road directions:

Ground is very close to roundabout where A57 meets A60. From this roundabout take A60 Newcastle Avenue into town centre. Turn left into Stubbing Lane, and immediately right into Central Avenue. Entrance to ground is 0.25 miles along, opposite Allen Street.

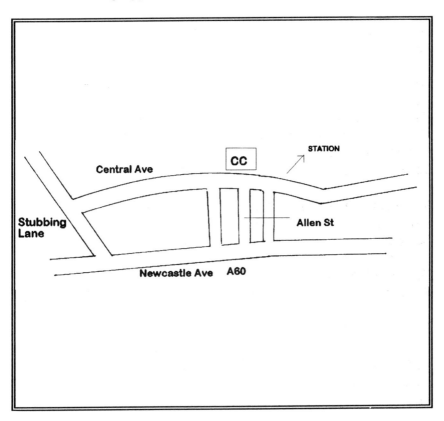

CRICKET MEMORABILIA
SOCIETY

Founded in April 1987

**Over 800 members
worldwide**

**Annual Subscription: £10
Senior citizens: £6
Youth(under 18): £2
Overseas airmail: £5 extra**

**For further information,
write to:
Mr T. Sheldon
29, Highclere Road
Crumpsall,
Manchester M8 4WH**

A Society for Collectors

The Pavilion at Trent Bridge (PDL)

County cricket at Taunton (RO)

The Cricket Society

Offers :

- **P**ublications - biannual journal and news bulletin eight times a year
- **M**onthly meetings addressed by prominent cricket personalities, held in Bath, Birmingham, Durham and London
- **T**op class Dinners
- **C**omprehensive cricket library
- **A**nnual coaching scholarships for youngsters and Kwik Cricket schools competition
- **C**ricket Society playing XI
- **C**ricketers Service held annually at St Johns Wood Church, London
- **A**nnual awards presented for outstanding play and for the best cricket publication

Whether you want to play the game, talk about it, watch it, read about it, write about it, encourage it. .. **The Cricket Society** has something for you all for 25p a week !

Annual Subscriptions: Full £13
Senior Citizen £9
Junior £9
Family £18.50

For further information or details of how you can join over 2000 existing members around the World, please contact:
Eric Budd, Honorary Secretary,
16 Storey Court,
39 St John's Wood Road, London NW8 8QX.
Tel: 0171 820 1866 (Work) or 0171 286 7054 (Home)

Somerset CCC

Club address: The Clerical Medical County Ground, St James's Street, Taunton, Somerset, TA1 1JT

Telephone: 01823-272946   **Fax:** 01823-332395

Ticket Office: As above

Other telephone numbers:

Marketing Department: 01823-337598

Club shop: 01823-337597

Centre of cricketing excellence: 01823- 352266

Rapid Cricketline: 0891-567513

Grounds: Taunton - County Ground
Bath - The Recreation Ground

1997 Membership Subscriptions:

Full:	£68
2nd full:	£52

(living in same household, also member of full member's family)

Country:	£46
Junior:	£20

(under 18 on 1/1/97, includes Junior Members' Club)

Young persons (18-21):	£27
Senior citizen:	£46
Family:	£124

(2 adults & 1 child. Additional children £10 each)

Vice President:	£77
2nd Vice President:	£62

(living in same household, also member of Vice President's family)

Vice President Family:	£145

(2 adults & 1 child. Additional children £10 each)

Executive Business club: £470+VAT

Company Patron:	£155 + VAT

(2 transferable tickets)

Each additional ticket: £75 + VAT

Reciprocal arrangements:

Admission to members' areas when Somerset CCC is playing away, after paying ground admission charge.

Admission to members' areas at Gloucestershire & Glamorgan home matches after paying ground admission charge.

(Subject to discretion of home club)

Ground admission reductions given for:

Senior citizens:	Yes
School students:	Yes
Up to age:	16
Unemployed:	No
Students:	No

Supporters Club:
Somerset Wyverns, Chris Green
13 Cooper Close, Aylestone,
Leicester, LE2 8ST

Corporate entertaining:
Facilities available for wedding
receptions, dinner dances, meetings

and other functions. Contact the
Catering Manager for details.
Facilities also available at matches -
contact club for details.

Visually impaired people:
No reduced admission. Guide dogs
allowed.

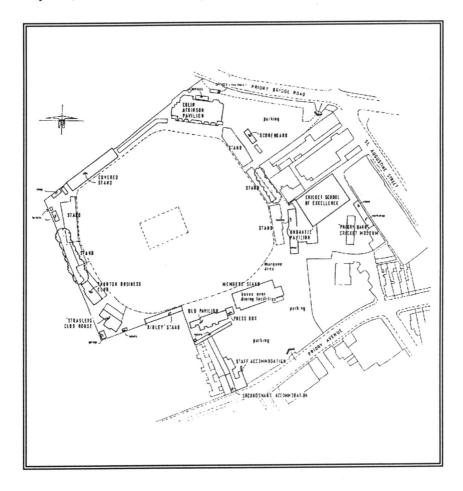

Taunton plan - courtesy Somerset CCC

Somerset CCC
County Ground: Taunton

Description of ground: Cricket at Taunton is close to the town centre, within easy walking distance of the ground - enclosed between St. James's St, the River Tone, Priory Bridge Road, and the Cattle Market. The red sandstone tower of St.James's in one corner, Colin Atkinson pavilion, and Stragglers opposite, country cider, the hustle and bustle of people coming and going are all part of sparkling West Country cricket.

Address: St. James's Street, Taunton, Somerset, TA1 1JT
Telephone: 01823-272946
Capacity: 6,000 (can be expanded for cup matches)

General facilities:
Club shop: Yes
Club museum: Yes
Cricket coaching facilities: Yes. Indoor school.
Cricket nets: Yes
Other sporting or recreational facilities on the ground: No
Facilities for hire or wider community use at the ground: Rooms for wedding receptions, dinners, meetings etc.

Facilities and access for people with disabilities:
Wheelchair access to the ground: Yes
Designated car parking available inside the ground: Yes
Good viewing areas inside the ground for people using wheelchairs: Yes
Designated viewing areas: Yes
Match commentaries for visually handicapped people: Yes (on request)
Ramps to provide easy access to bars and refreshment outlets: At most

Food & drink:

	Members	General Public
Full restaurant/dining facilities:	Yes	No
Food suitable for vegetarians:	Yes	Yes
Bars:	2	1

Travel:
Car parking: Vice President members and disabled only at ground. Local car parks, and at Rugby Ground.
Nearest station: Taunton.

Buses: Very near bus station. Information: 01823-272033
Tourist information: Taunton TIC, Paul Street, TA1 3PF. 01823-336344. Fax: 01823-340308.

Road directions:
Well sign posted from the M5. Take junction 25, A358 and join A38 towards town centre. At roundabout take Priory Avenue (A3038), straight over next roundabout, into Priory Bridge Road, and ground is on left.

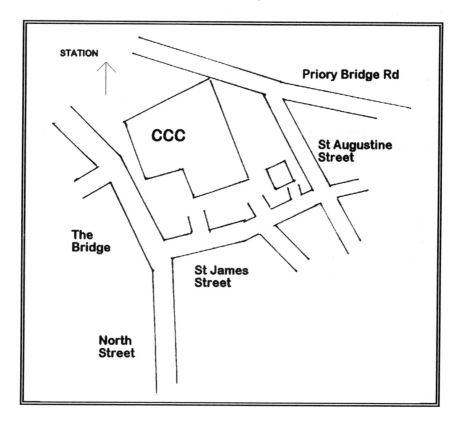

Somerset CCC
Bath Recreation Ground

Description of ground: With Weston Super Mare now gone, Bath provides the only remaining Somerset cricket festival. The Recreation Ground is in the city centre besides the Avon, opposite the Great Abbey. Very attractive venue, with marquees for distinguished guests and refreshments. Plenty of room for strolling around and enjoying the various sightings of the city.

Address: The Pavilion, The Recreation Ground, William St, Bath
Telephone: 01225-424970   **Capacity:** 6,000

General facilities:
Club shop: Yes
Club museum: No
Cricket coaching facilities: No
Cricket nets: No
Other sporting or recreational facilities on the ground: Contact local council.

Facilities for hire or wider community use at the ground: Contact local council
Other sporting recreational or leisure activities: Contact local council. Sports and leisure centre at ground.

Food & drink:

	Members	General Public
Full restaurant/dining facilities:	Yes	No
Food suitable for vegetarians:	Yes	Yes
Bars:	2	1

Facilities and access for people with disabilities:
Wheelchair access to the ground: Yes
Designated car parking available inside the ground: Yes
Good viewing areas inside the ground for people using wheelchairs: Yes
Designated viewing areas: Yes
Ramps to provide easy access to bars and refreshment outlets: Not necessary

Travel:

Car parking: At ground: members £3, public £5. Also local car parks, and park and ride (except Saturdays)

Nearest station: Bath Spa

Buses: Information: 01225-464446

Tourist information: Bath TIC, Abbey Chambers, Abbey Church Yard, BA1 1LY. 01225-477101. Fax: 01225-477221.

Road directions:

Ground is off A36 (Pultney Road) to east of city centre. Turn into Edward St at roundabout, and then left into Pulteney Mews. If coming along Great Pultney Street, turn into William Street, and then into Pulteney Mews. Entrance from city centre from Argyle Street via Pulteney Bridge and right after the shops and do not confuse with Bath Cricket Club ground on the other side of North Parade.

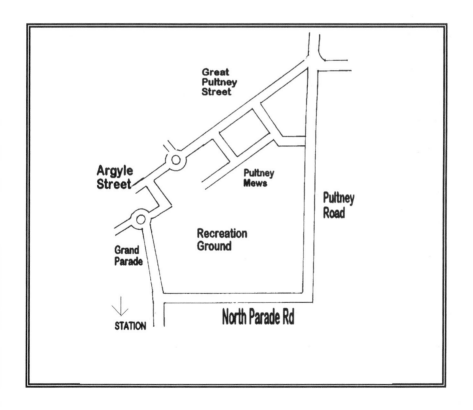

Surrey CCC

Club address: The Foster's Oval, The Oval, Kennington , London, SE11 5SS
Telephone: 0171-582-6660   **Fax:** 0171-735-7769
Ticket Office: 0171-582-7764
Other telephone numbers:
Ken Barrington Cricket Centre (The Foster's Oval): As above
Surrey County Cricket Centre (Guildford): 01483-59880. Fax: 01483-59881
The Foster's Oval Shop: 0171-820-1866. Fax: 0171-735-7769
Rapid Cricketline: 0891-567514
Grounds: The Foster's Oval
            Guildford - Guildford CC

1997 Membership Subscriptions:
County:

Full:	£90
Country:	£55
Junior Season Ticket:	£10
(17 and under on 31/12/96)	
Youth (18-23):	£55
Senior citizen(65 and over):	£55

International:
Includes free admission to all Surrey matches, & International matches at The Foster's Oval (booking necessary to guarantee). 10 free guest passes per season for Championship and Sunday League matches. A waiting list operates for this category. It is imperative to become a County member first.

Adult:	£195
Senior Citizen (65 and over):	£170
Overseas:	£55

Except for Junior Season Ticket, new members pay £30 joining fee.

Country members are 50 miles from The Foster's Oval.

Executive Suite Membership and Group Membership - contact Marketing Department for availability. Usually fully subscribed.

Reciprocal arrangements:
After paying ground admission charge, use of members' facilities at away grounds when Surrey CCC is playing.

Use of members' facilities at Sydney Cricket Ground and Newlands (Cape Town) Cricket Ground

118

Ground admission reductions given for:

Senior citizens: Yes
School students: Yes
Up to age: 17
Unemployed: Yes
Students: Yes

Supporters Club:
Ms Sarah Atkins, Surrey CCC Supporters' Club, 236 Ashbourne Road, Mitcham, Surrey, CR4 2DR 0181-648-2800.

Corporate entertaining:
The Foster's Oval has different size function rooms available for hire, including a banqueting suite. There are also conference and training facilities. Different meals are also available. Contact the Meeting Point office for details. Corporate entertaiing facilities also available for county matches.

Visually impaired people:
Reduced admission county matches only. No guide dogs allowed.

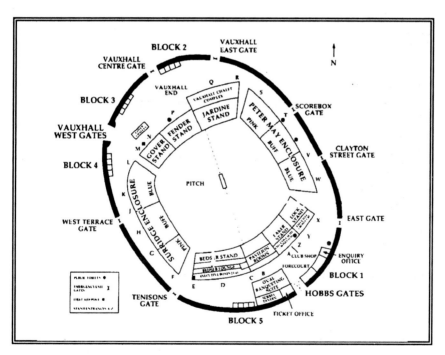

The Foster's Oval plan - courtesy Surrey CCC

119

Surrey CCC
The Foster's Oval

Description of ground: Modern Test match ground, with the famous gas holders next door on one side, and Archbishop Tenison school on the other. Very good facilities. Look out for the new clock. First used by Surrey in 1845. Has also staged an FA Cup Final. The local underground station is named after the ground. Very different from Lords in middle class St John's Wood - the immediate area is mainly inner city council flats, where the roofs and balconies sometimes provide an unoffical view of big matches.

Address: The Oval, Kennington, London, SE11 5SS
Telephone: 0171-582-6660   **Capacity:** 17,000

General facilities
Club shop: Yes
Club museum: No
Cricket coaching facilities: Yes
Cricket nets: Ken Barrington Cricket centre.
Other sporting or recreational facilities on the ground: Health & fitness club.

Facilities for hire or wider community use at the ground: Conference rooms, banqueting facilities etc.
Other sporting recreational / leisure activities: Occasional use - Australian rules football, baseball.

Facilities and access for people with disabilities:
Wheelchair access to the ground: Yes
Designated car parking available inside the ground: Yes
Good viewing areas inside the ground for people using wheelchairs: Yes
Designated viewing areas: Yes
Ramps to provide easy access to bars and refreshment outlets: Yes

Food & drink:

	Members	General Public
Full restaurant/dining facilities:	Yes	Yes
Food suitable for vegetarians:	Yes	Yes
Bars:	2	3

Travel:

Car parking: None at ground except for disabled - check with club. Street parking very limited, and up to 0.5 miles from Ground. *Nearest station:* The Oval (London Underground) Vauxhall (South West trains) *Buses:* 0171-222-1234 *Tourist information:* 0839-123456 (premium rate). Tourist information centres at Victoria station and Liverpool St station.

Road directions:

The ground is just south of Vauxhall Bridge on the A202, Vauxhall Road. It is also by the junction of the A3 and A23. The ground is on the A3 (Kennington Park Road) is about a mile south of Elephant and Castle. Look out for the Oval station.

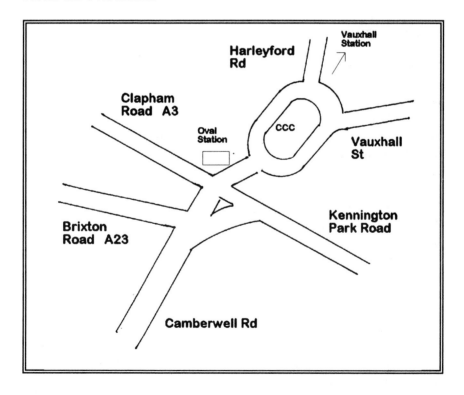

Surrey CCC
Guildford Cricket Club

Description of ground: Club ground with modern pavilion. Also home to local hockey club. First Surrey match in 1938, against Hampshire. Very near town centre.

Address: Woodbridge Road, Guildford, Surrey, GU1
Telephone: 01483-572181   **Capacity:** 3,500

General facilities:
Club shop: Yes
Club museum: No
Cricket coaching facilities: No
Cricket nets: Contact club

Other sporting or recreational facilities on the ground: Hockey
Facilities for hire or wider community use at the ground: No

Facilities and access for people with disabilities:
Wheelchair access to the ground: Yes
Designated car parking available inside the ground: Yes
Good viewing areas inside the ground for people using wheelchairs: Yes
Designated viewing areas: Yes
Ramps to provide easy access to bars and refreshment outlets: Yes

Food & drink:

	Members	General Public
Full restaurant/dining facilities:	No	No
Food suitable for vegetarians:	Yes	Yes
Bars:	1	1

Travel:
Car parking: Limited at ground. Some at Guildford Technical College - Stoke Rd. Also local car parks. Very limited street parking.
Nearest station: Guildford

Buses: Information: 01483-575226
Tourist information: Guildford TIC, 14, Tunsgate, GU1 3QT. 01483-444333. Fax: 01483: 302046.

Road directions:
From A3 south, take A3100 turn off into Guildford. At roundabout, go west on A25. Go straight over roundabout with A320, and take next left at traffic lights, Woodbridge Road. Ground on right hand side.
From A3 north, turn off onto A25. Go east and turn right into Woodbridge Road. Ground on right hand side.

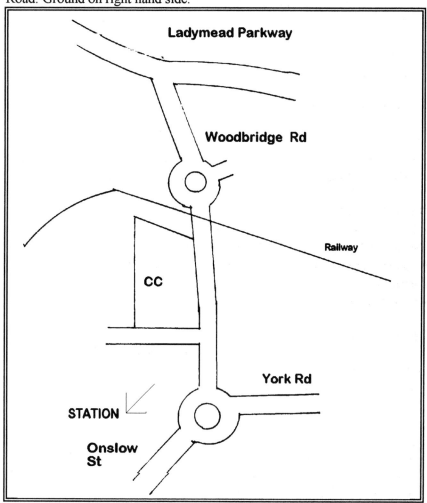

Sussex CCC

Club address: County Ground, Eaton Road, Hove, East Sussex, BN3 3AN
Telephone: 01273-732161   **Fax:** 01273-771549
Ticket Office: As above
Other telephone numbers:
Membership hotline: 01273-207208
Youth Development Office: 01273-735143
Rapid Cricketline: 0891-567515
Grounds: Hove - County Ground
          Arundel - Friends of Arundel Castle CC
          Eastbourne - Eastbourne Saffrons Sports Club
          Horsham - Horsham CC

1997 Membership Subscriptions:
Standard: £60
Associate: £18.50
(Use of members' facilities for most matches after paying ground admission)
Student / Junior: £15
(Student is under 23 at 1/1/97, and in full-time education)
Business House: £240
(4 transferable tickets)
Affiliated Club: £27
(Priority booking for tickets, no use of members' facilities or admission to games without payment)

Other :
Adult guest ticket: £35
Junior guest ticket: £11

Membership can be commuted for 3 to 10 years.

No life membership available.

Reciprocal arrangements:
Admission to members' areas at Sussex CCC away matches, after payment of admission charge.

Free admission to Goodwood race course on 22 May 1997 and 6 June 1997.

Ground admission reductions given for:
Senior citizens: Yes
(Sunday League & Tourist match only)
School students (10-18):   Yes
Under 10:   Free
Unemployed: No
Students: No

Supporters Club:
Mr P. Watson, c/o Sussex CCC.

124

Corporate entertaining:
Hospitality boxes and marquees available for matches. Facilities also available for conferences, lunches, dinners, wedding receptions etc.

Visually impaired people:
Reduced admission - group bookings only. Guide dogs allowed.

Deckchairs at Hove (PDL)

Sport at Horsham (PDL)

Sussex CCC
County Ground: Hove

Description of ground: Some modern facilities combined with traditional areas, including deckchairs at one end. Very near the beach. Used by Sussex since 1872. A day at the sea, combined with a day at the cricket. Pavilion not far from the playing area, and includes marvellous pictures and other memorabilia of Sussex cricket history.

Address: County Ground, Eaton Road, Hove, East Sussex, BN3 3AN
Telephone: 01273-732161   **Capacity:** 5,000

General facilities:

Club shop: Yes
Club museum: No - but there is a library
Cricket coaching facilities: All year round. Indoor cricket school.
Cricket nets: All year round. Indoor cricket school.

Other sporting or recreational facilities on the ground: No
Facilities for hire or wider community use at the ground: Dining and conference facilities
Other: Mother and Baby room in indoor cricket school.

Facilities and access for people with disabilities:

Wheelchair access to the ground: Yes
Designated car parking available inside the ground: Yes
Good viewing areas inside the ground for people using wheelchairs: Yes
Designated viewing areas: Yes
Ramps to provide easy access to bars and refreshment outlets: No

Food & drink:

	Members	General Public
Full restaurant/dining facilities:	Yes	No
Food suitable for vegetarians:	Yes	Yes
Bars:	1	2.

Plus pub "The Sussex Cricketer" by main entrance.

Travel:

Car parking: Some for members at ground. Street parking and local car parks.

Nearest station: Hove. Brighton station is less than 1 mile away.

Buses: 7 from Hove station, 6 from Brighton station. Information: 01273-700406.

Tourist information: Hove TIC, King Alfred Leisure Centre, Kingsway, BN3 2WW. 01273-746100. Fax: 01273-746100.

Road directions:

A23 towards Brighton. Before reaching town, follow signs for A27, Hove/Worthing. Keep in left hand lane following signs to Hove. At roundabout, take second exit to Brighton (Dyke Rd). Turn right into Woodland Drive, and left into Shirley Drive This becomes The Drive. Turn left into Eaton Road, and ground is on left.

Driving along the sea front, from Brighton Town Centre, pass West Pier (closed) and turn right up Grand Avenue. Take second right into Eaton Road, and ground is on left.

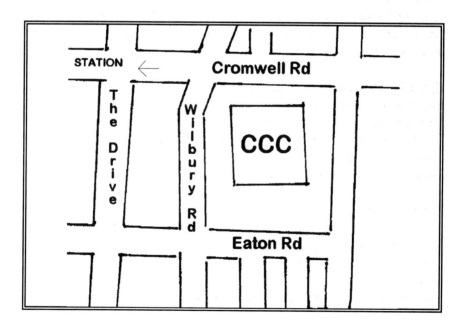

Sussex CCC
Friends of Arundel Castle CC

Description of ground: Stunning setting in Castle grounds. Traditionally hosts the tourists' first game. The ground was built by the 15th Duke of Norfolk in 1895. One of the most famous venues for festival cricket - and an ideal choice to provide part of the title for this book!

Address: Arundel Park, Arundel, E.Sussex, BN18 9LH
Telephone: 01903-882462   **Capacity:** 9,000

General facilities:
Club shop: Yes
Club museum: No
Cricket coaching facilities: Yes - contact club
Cricket nets: Yes - contact club. Indoor cricket school.

Other sporting or recreational facilities on the ground: No
Facilities for hire or wider community use at the ground: No
Other sporting recreational / leisure activities: No

Facilities and access for people with disabilities:
Wheelchair access to the ground: Yes
Designated car parking available inside the ground: Yes
Good viewing areas inside the ground for people using wheelchairs: Yes
Designated viewing areas: Yes
Ramps to provide easy access to bars and refreshment outlets: No

Food & drink:

	Members	General Public
Full restaurant/dining facilities:	Yes	No
Food suitable for vegetarians:	Yes	Yes
Bars:	1	1

Travel:
Car parking: In ground £4. Do not park by the Castle entrance - it's a long walk.

Nearest station: Arundel
Buses: 11 from station. Information: 01903-237661

Tourist information: Arundel TIC,   01903-882268.
61, High St BN18 9AJ.   Fax: 01903-882419

Road directions:

From A27, turn north at roundabout with A284 (direction Petworth), then first right into London Road and entrance to ground is on left.

From A29, take A284 into Arundel, turn left into London Road, and entrance to ground is on left.

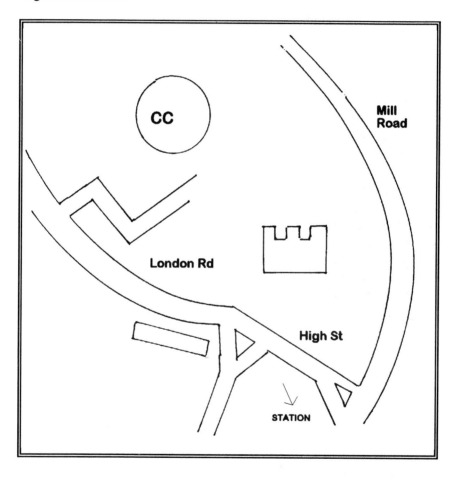

Sussex CCC
Eastbourne Saffrons Sports Club

Description of ground: Cricket at the Saffrons since 1867 is some way from the sea front and part of a recreation ground also providing football and bowls. Scene of the great and highly improbable defeat of Armstrong's Australians in 1921; trees and hills surround the ground, and marquees and deck chairs make attractive summer scene.

Address: Eastbourne Saffrons Sports Club, The Saffrons, Compton Place Road, Eastbourne, E.Sussex, BN21 1EA
Telephone: 01323-724328   **Capacity:** 4,500

General facilities
Club shop: Yes
Club museum: No
Cricket coaching facilities: No
Cricket nets: No
Other sporting or recreational

facilities on the ground: Hockey, football, croquet, squash - for members.
Facilities for hire or wider community use at the ground: No

Facilities and access for people with disabilities
Wheelchair access to the ground: Yes
Designated car parking available inside the ground: No
Good viewing areas inside the ground for people using wheelchairs: Yes
Designated viewing areas: No
Ramps to provide easy access to bars and refreshment outlets: No

Food & drink:

	Members	General Public
Full restaurant/dining facilities:	Yes	No
Food suitable for vegetarians:	Yes	No
Bars:	1	1

Travel:
Car parking: Inside ground £4.
Nearest station: Eastbourne

Buses: Near Central Coach station.
Information: 01323-416416

Tourist information: Eastbourne   01323-411400.
TIC, Cornfield Rd, BN21 4QL.   Fax: 01323-649574.

Road directions:

From A27 and A22: Come into Eastbourne on A22 (Willingdon Rd). This becomes Upperton Rd. At roundabout, turn right into Grove Road. Turn right at end of road, and right again into Saffrons Road. The ground is very close to the town hall and the courts.

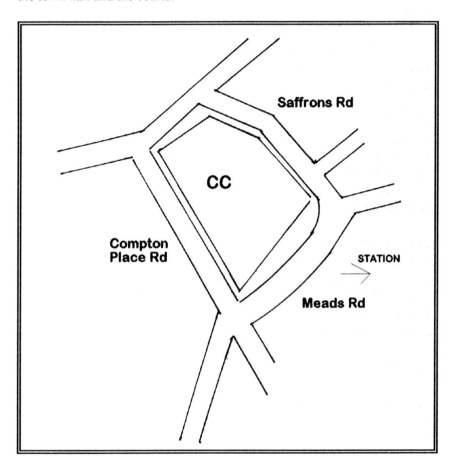

Sussex CCC
Horsham Cricket Club

Description of ground: Pleasant club ground with modern pavilion, also used for other sports as hockey, squash and tennis. South of town centre. Sussex played Essex here in 1908, and have used the ground on and off ever since.

Address: Cricketfield Road, Worthing Road, Horsham, W.Sussex, RH12 1TE
Telephone: 01403-254628   **Capacity:** 4,500

General facilities:
Club shop: Yes
Club museum: No
Cricket coaching facilities: Contact club
Cricket nets: Contact club

Other sporting or recreational facilities on the ground: Hockey, squash & tennis for club members
Facilities for hire or wider community use at the ground: No

Facilities and access for people with disabilities:
Wheelchair access to the ground: Yes
Designated car parking available inside the ground: No
Good viewing areas inside the ground for people using wheelchairs: Yes
Designated viewing areas: No
Ramps to provide easy access to bars and refreshment outlets: No

Food & drink:

	Members	General Public
Full restaurant/dining facilities:	Yes	No
Food suitable for vegetarians:	Yes	No
Bars:	1	1

Travel:
Car parking: In ground £4.
Nearest station: Horsham
Buses: Information: 0345-959099

Tourist information: Horsham TIC, 9, Causeway, RH12 1HE. 01403-211661. Fax: 01403-215268.

Road directions:
From A24 Horsham by pass, take A281 towards town centre. Turn right into Blackbridge Lane. At end of road, turn left into Worthing Road, and then immediately right into Cricketfield Road. Ground on right.

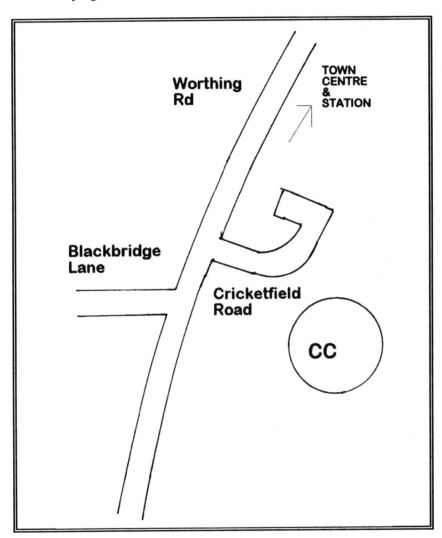

Warwickshire CCC

Club address: County Ground, Edgbaston Road, Edgbaston, Birmingham, B5 7QU
Telephone: 0121-446-4422
Fax: 0121-446-4544
Ticket Office: 0121-446-5506
Other telephone numbers:
Club Shop: 0121-446-4787
Exhibitions / Catering / Functions: 0121-440-0747
Marketing Department: 0121-446-4777
Rapid Cricketline: 0891-567516
Grounds: Edgbaston - County Ground

1997 Membership Subscriptions:

Full:
Town:	£74
Senior Town:	£40
Country:	£60
Senior Country:	£35

Husband and wife:
Town:	£95
Senior:	£57
Country:	£76
Child/grandchild:*	£14
Student:	£28

(18 and under 23 - on 1/5/97 - and in full-time education)

Junior Season Ticket:*	£20

*Includes free membership of Warwickshire Junior Bears Club aged 8 - 14

Patron:
(Includes transferable guest card, junior card and car park ticket)

Town:	£139
Country:	£108
Senior:	£83

Disabled (wheelchair users): £20 (Free card issued for a helper if necessary)

Country membership is defined as 15 miles from Edgbaston.

Joining fee: £30. Senior: £20. Not applicable to student members and junior season ticket holders.

Executive and Company membership also available.

Reciprocal arrangements:
Admission to members' areas at Warwickshire CCC away matches, after payment of admission charges.

134

Uttoxeter racecourse: Discounted entry to Daily Club and Members' enclosure.

Ground admission reductions given for:
(County matches only)

Senior citizens:	Yes
School students:	Yes
Up to age:	16
Unemployed:	Yes
Students:	Yes
Disabled (wheelchair users):	Yes

Supporters Club:
Coaches arranged for away fixtures.

Bookings through club office as above.

Corporate entertaining:
For matches, private boxes and suites available for hire.
Other entertainment and conference facilities available - contact the Marketing Department for details.

Visually impaired people:
Free admission except for international matches. Not for helpers any matches. Guide dogs allowed.

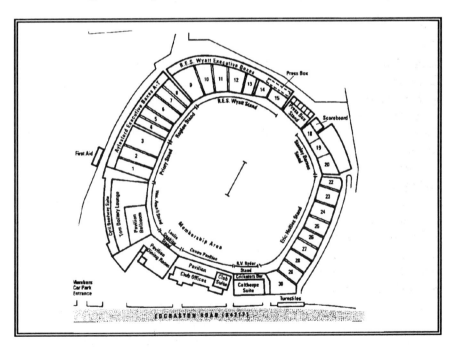

Edgbaston plan - courtesy Warwickshire CCC

Warwickshire CCC
County Ground: Edgbaston

Description of ground: Modern Test match ground with excellent facilities. Now only ground used by Warwickshire. First used by the County in 1894, and first staged a Test match in 1902. Used as a Test match venue until 1929, but then not again until 1957. The rejuvenation of the club and ground produced an extraordinary architectural collection of buildings known at the Pavilion Suite and including the pavilion, bars, dining rooms, executive suites and ball rooms. Buzz and enterprise continues with remarkable success on the field and circulation areas are spacious and full of fun and activity on big occasions.

Address: Edgbaston Road, Edgbaston, Birmingham, B5 7QU
Telephone: 0121-446-4422   **Capacity:** 20,000

General facilities:
Club shop: Yes
Club museum: Yes
Cricket coaching facilities: Yes. Juniors only in summer, juniors, adults & clubs in winter
Cricket nets: Yes - summer: youth representative teams only. Juniors, adults & clubs in winter
Other sporting or recreational facilities on the ground: No
Facilities for hire or wider community use at the ground: Function rooms for weddings, conferences, dinners etc.

Facilities and access for people with disabilities:
Designated car parking available inside the ground: Yes
Good viewing areas inside the ground for people using wheelchairs: Yes
Designated viewing areas: Yes
Ramps to provide easy access to bars and refreshment outlets: No - lift access to some areas

Food & drink:

	Members	General Public
Full restaurant/dining facilities:	Yes	Some matches only
Food suitable for vegetarians:	Yes	Yes
Bars: At least 4 public bars for Tests	2	1

Travel:

Car parking: Some for members at ground. Usually parking in Calthorpe Park, and local car parks.
Nearest station: Birmingham New Street (1 mile)
Buses: 45 & 47 from city centre.

1 from Fiveways / Hagley Rd. Information: 0121-200-2700
Tourist information: Birmingham Convention & Visitor Bureau, 2, City Arcade, B2 4TX. 0121-643-2514. Fax: 0121-616-1038.

Road directions:

From city centre, take A441 south, turn left into Edgbaston Road (B4217), and ground is on right. Well sign posted from M6. Use ring road to link up with A441 from other directions.

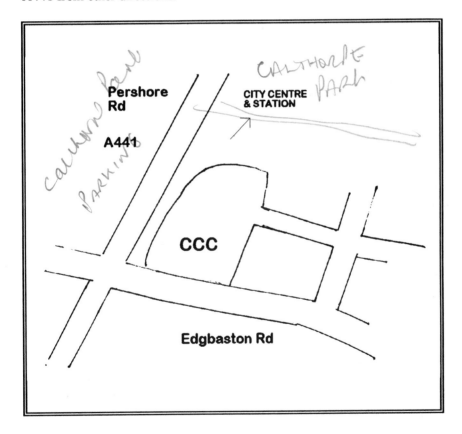

Worcestershire CCC

Club address: County Ground, New Road, Worcester, WR2 4QQ
Telephone: 01905-748474   **Fax:** 01905-748005
Ticket Office: As above
Other telephone numbers:
Cricket Suite Caterers: 01905-432561 or 01905-420274 (Tel/fax)
Supporters Association: 01905-424739
Rapid Cricketline: 0891-567517
Grounds: Worcester - County Ground
          Kidderminster - Kidderminster CC

1997 Membership Subscriptions:

Full Member:	£75
Country Member:	£65
Junior member (under 18):	£20
(Includes Black Pears Club)	
Senior citizen:	£55
Senior citizen (country):	£49
(Senior citizen is over 60)	
Patron Member:	£140
Patron Member (country):	£117
(Patron member includes one guest)	
Patron and car:	£182
Patron and car (country):	£148
Company and car:	£184
(2 transferable passes)	
Member's car pass:	£47
Member's car pass: (country):	£37

Life membership also available.

Country membership defined as 20 miles from the County Ground.

Reciprocal arrangements:

Use of members facilities at grounds where Worcestershire are playing away.

Ground admission reductions given for:

Senior citizens:	Yes
School students:	Yes
Up to age:	17 and under
Children under 7:	Free
Unemployed:	Yes
Students:	Yes

Supporters Association:

Worcestershire CC Supporters Association, County Ground, New Road, Worcester WR2 4QQ.
Travel arranged for away matches - Pat Mills: 01905-424739.

Visually impaired people:

Reduced admission on request, including helper. Guide dogs allowed. Give one day's warning.

Cricket and the Cathedral at Worcester (RO)

Festival cricket, Kidderminster (RO)

Worcestershire CCC
County Ground: Worcester

Description of ground: With majestic Worcester Cathedral besides the River Severn, New Road is one of the most charming cricket grounds. Within easy walking distance of the city centre across the Severn bridge. The dignified members' pavilion (1898) shows little external change and with the adjacent Ladies' Pavilion sits hospitably besides the trees, and don't miss the teas.

Address: County Ground, New Road, Worcester, WR2 4QQ
Telephone: 01905-748474   **Capacity:** 4,500

General facilities:

Club shop: Yes

Club museum: No

Cricket coaching facilities: No

Cricket nets: No

Other sporting or recreational facilities on the ground: No

Facilities for hire or wider community use at the ground: Yes

Facilities and access for people with disabilities:
Wheelchair access to the ground: Yes
Designated car parking available inside the ground: Yes
Good viewing areas inside the ground for people using wheelchairs: Yes
Designated viewing areas: Yes
Ramps to provide easy access to bars and refreshment outlets: Yes

Food & drink:

	Members	General Public
Full restaurant/dining facilities:	Yes	Yes
Food suitable for vegetarians:	Yes	Yes
Bars:	1	1

Travel:
Car parking: Ground: members with season passes only. Sundays: Christopher Whitehead school - free for car park pass holders, £1.50 for others.
Nearest station: Worcester (Foregate St)

Buses: 23, 44, 46.
Information: 0345-125436
Tourist information: Worcester

TIC, The Guildhall, High Street,
WR1 2EY. 01905-726311.
Fax: 01905-722028

Road directions:

AA signs for Worcester Races are prominent but follow them for the City Centre. Take Bridge Street (A38), and go left over the bridge. For adjacent to ground parking, go immediately left behind garage. For Ground, continue on A44, down New Road, and Ground is on left.

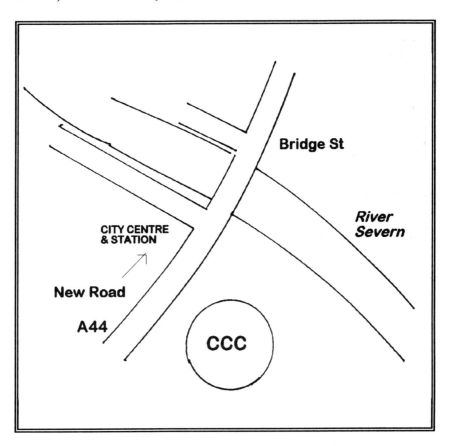

Worcestershire CCC
Kidderminster Cricket Club

Description of ground: Kidderminster Cricket Club was established in 1890 and after playing championship matches there for 52 years between 1921 and 1973, the county resumed for one match a season from 1987. Essentially an urban setting with housing surrounds and a few trees but marquees and deck chairs make for a festival atmosphere. Original pavilion (1896) immaculate. On approaching Ground, look hard for entrance up a winding path to parking.

Address: Chester Road Sports Club, Offmore Lane, Chester Rd, Kidderminster, DY10 1TH
Telephone: 01562-824175   **Capacity:** 3,000 - can be expanded

General facilities:
Club shop: Yes
Club museum: No
Cricket coaching facilities: Yes - club members only
Cricket nets: Yes - members only
Other sporting or recreational facilities on the ground: Hockey, snooker

Facilities for hire or wider community use at the ground: Function room
Other sporting recreational / leisure activities: Worcestershire CCC second XI, county association, and international police matches

Facilities and access for people with disabilities:
Wheelchair access to the ground: Yes
Designated car parking available inside the ground: Yes
Good viewing areas inside the ground for people using wheelchairs: Yes
Designated viewing areas: Yes
Ramps to provide easy access to bars and refreshment outlets: Yes

Food & drink:

	Members	General Public
Full restaurant/dining facilities:	Yes	By prior arrangement
Food suitable for vegetarians:	Yes	Yes
Bars:	1	1

Travel:

Car parking: In ground for members and public - £2.50 without members' car park pass. Also local street parking.

Nearest station: Kidderminster (0.5 miles)

Buses: Hopper buses from town centre.

Tourist information: Kidderminster TIC, Severn Valley Railway Station, Comberton Hill, DY10 1QX. 01562-829400.

Road directions:

No yellow AA signs. From M5 junction 3, A456 towards town centre, turn left into Chester Road, and Ground on left. Ground is just to east of town centre, by Comberton estate.

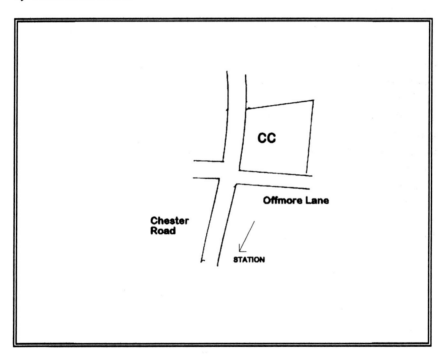

Yorkshire CCC

Club address: Headingley Cricket Ground, St Michael's Lane, Leeds, West Yorkshire, LS6 3BU

Telephone: 0113-278-7394   **Fax:** 0113-278-4099

Ticket Office: As above

Other telephone numbers:

Rapid Cricketline: 0891-567518

Whiterose shop: 0113-275-3290

Grounds: Leeds - Headingley
Scarborough - Scarborough CC

1997 Membership Subscriptions:

Full member & spouse: *	£66
Country member & spouse: *	£44
Junior (under 18):	£23
Junior Tykes:	£15
Student (18 or over):	£37
Retired member & spouse: *	£44
Overseas:	£44
Affiliated club & spouse: *	£66

* or junior

Corporate member & spouse: £84
(or junior) Tickets transferable

Corporate additional ticket: £44

Up to age:	17 and under
Unemployed:	No
Students:	No

Supporters Association:

Secretary: Martin Wraith, 19, Staybrite Avenue, Cottingley, Bingley BD16 1PR. 01274-562468.

Yorkshire CCC Southern Group: David Wood, 15, Rothschild Road, Linslade, Leighton Buzzard, LU7 7SY. 01525-370204.

Reciprocal arrangements:

Admission to members' areas at Yorkshire CCC away matches, after payment of admission charges.

Free admission to Yorkshire race courses on designated days.

Corporate entertaining:

Corporate entertaining facilities available at matches. Also facilities for conferences, training events, dinners etc. Contact the Marketing Department for details.

Ground admission reductions given for:

Senior citizens:	Yes
School students:	Yes

Visually impaired people:

Free admission including helper. Guide dogs allowed. Give a few days warning.

144

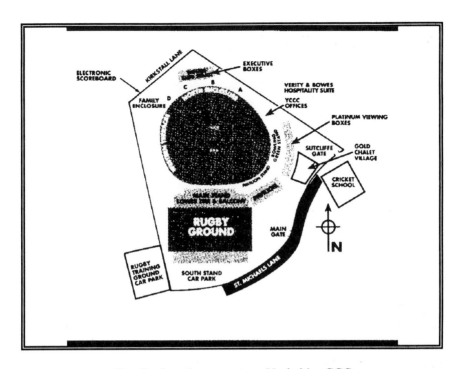

Headingley plan - courtesy Yorkshire CCC

England v South Africa - this time at Rugby League (PDL)

145

TMS at Headingley (PDL)

The Pavilion at Scarborough (PDL)

Yorkshire CCC
Headingley

Description of ground: Historic Test match ground, shared with Leeds Rugby League Club. One stand serves both Cricket and Rugby grounds. First used by Yorkshire in 1891. Some modernisation has taken place, but investment is restricted as Yorkshire CCC do not own the ground; a move is on the cards.

Address: Headingley Cricket Ground, St Michael's Lane, Leeds, LS6 3BU
Telephone: 0113-278-7394   **Capacity:** 15,500

General facilities:
Club shop: Yes
Club museum: No
Cricket coaching facilities: Indoor cricket school
Cricket nets: Indoor cricket school
Other sporting or recreational facilities on the ground: Rugby League and Rugby Union
Facilities for hire or wider community use at the ground: Facilities for wedding receptions, conferences, banquets etc.

Facilities and access for people with disabilities:
Wheelchair access to the ground: Yes
Designated car parking available inside the ground: Contact club
Good viewing areas inside the ground for people using wheelchairs: Yes
Designated viewing areas: Yes
Ramps to provide easy access to bars and refreshment outlets: Yes

Food & drink:

	Members	General Public
Full restaurant/dining facilities:	Yes	No
Food suitable for vegetarians:	Yes	Yes
Bars:	2	Up to 4

Travel:
Road restrictions on match days: Streets near ground. No parking for major matches.

Car parking: Very limited at ground. Some in local streets.
Nearest station: Headingley

Information: 0113-244-8133
Buses: 1, 28, 56, 57, 63, 93, 96.
Information: 0113-245-7676
Special transport arrangements on match days: Park and ride for

Test matches
Tourist information: Gateway Yorkshire, Station Arcade, PO Box 244, LS1 1PL. 0113-242-5242. Fax: 0113-246-8246

Road directions:

From south, east: M1 junction 47, then M621 junction 2 A643 towards city centre. Join A58(M) and follow signs for A660 (Otley, Skipton). Join A660, which becomes Headingley Lane. Turn left into North Lane, and ground is on left. *From west:* M62 junction 27 take M621 to junction 2, then as above.

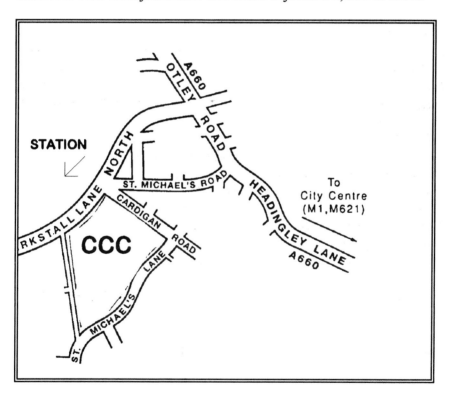

Yorkshire CCC
Scarborough Cricket Club

Description of ground: Home of the Scarborough Festival in early September. Very good facilities, better than some County grounds. First used by Yorkshire in 1878. Every cricket follower should visit Scarborough to see this historic home of northern cricket.

Address: North Marine Road, Scarborough, N.Yorkshire, YO12 7TJ
Telephone: 01723-365625. Fax: 01723-364287. **Capacity:** 15,000

General facilities:
Club shop: Yes
Club museum: No
Cricket coaching facilities: Contact club
Cricket nets: Contact club

Other sporting or recreational facilities on the ground: No
Facilities for hire or wider community use at the ground: No

Facilities and access for people with disabilities:
Wheelchair access to the ground: Yes
Designated car parking available inside the ground: No
Good viewing areas inside the ground for people using wheelchairs: Yes
Designated viewing areas: Yes
Ramps to provide easy access to bars and refreshment outlets: Yes

Food & drink:

	Members	General Public
Full restaurant/dining facilities:	No	No
Food suitable for vegetarians:	No	No
Bars:	1	2

Travel:
Car parking: None at ground. Local car parks and limited street parking.

Nearest station: Scarborough.
Buses: Bus station in town centre. 01723-375463.

Tourist information: Scarborough
TIC, Unit 3, Pavilion House, Valley
Bridge Rd, YO11 1UY.

01723-373333.
Fax: 01723-363785.

Road directions:
From town centre, take Victoria Road towards North Sands and North Bay.
This becomes Castle Road, and at roundabout, take North Marine Road on the
left. Ground on left 300 yards further on.

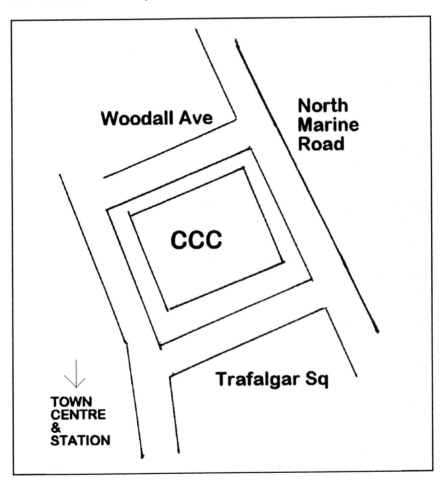

Cambridge University CC

Club ground: Fenner's, Mortimer Road, Cambridge.
Club address: Prof. K.Siddle (Hon. Treasurer), Clinical Biochemistry, Box 232 , Addenbrooke's Hospital, Hills Road, Cambridge CB2 2QR
Tel: 01223-315925 or 01223-353552 (Ground).
     01223-336789 (Hon. Treasurer)   **Fax:** 01223-331157
Ticket Office: As above
Other telephone numbers: None

Membership:

Life membership:	£60
Five years:	£30
One year:	£12

Reductions given for:

Senior citizens:	Yes
School students:	Yes
Unemployed:	Yes
Students:	Yes

Reciprocal arrangements: None (most matches are played at Fenner's)

Ground admission:
Free, except for Benson and Hedges British Universities games and matches involving touring teams.

When Ground admission is charged, reductions given for:

Senior citizens:	Yes
School students:	Yes
Unemployed:	No
Students:	Yes

Supporters Club:
None, but a coach is run to Lords for the varsity match.

Other information:
Cambridgeshire CCC play some minor counties matches at Fenner's.

The club publish a newsletter, *Cover Point,* which is on sale in the pavilion.

Cambridge University CC
Fenner's

Description of ground: New pavilion, but very little other development. Very pleasant university setting in classical Cambridge. Modern flats overlook one corner. Very limited facilities for spectators, but bring a deck chair and watch the cricket on a sunny day.

Address: Mortimer Road, Cambridge. **Telephone:** 01223-353552

General facilities:
Club shop: No
Club museum: No
Cricket coaching facilities: No
Cricket nets: No
Other sporting or recreational facilities on the ground: No
Facilities for hire or wider community use at the ground: Yes. Pavilion can be hired for functions, and ground for matches.

Facilities and access for people with disabilities:
Wheelchair access to the ground: Yes
Designated car parking available inside the ground: No
Good viewing areas inside the ground for people using wheelchairs: Yes
Designated viewing areas: No
Ramps to provide easy access to bars and refreshment outlets: No.
No toilets for people with disabilities

Food & drink:

	Members	General Public
Full restaurant/dining facilities:	Yes	No
Food suitable for vegetarians:	Yes	Yes
Bars:	1	1

Travel:
Car parking: Free for members. Multi storey car park by ground.
Nearest station: Cambridge
Buses: Any for city centre

Tourist information: Cambridge TIC, Wheeler St, CB2 3QB. Tel: 01223-322640. Fax: 01223-463385

153

Road directions:
Ground is in city centre, by traffic lights where Gonville Place (A603) meets Mill Road. A603 from M11 junction 12 or A1134 from M11 junction 11 lead to Gonville Place.

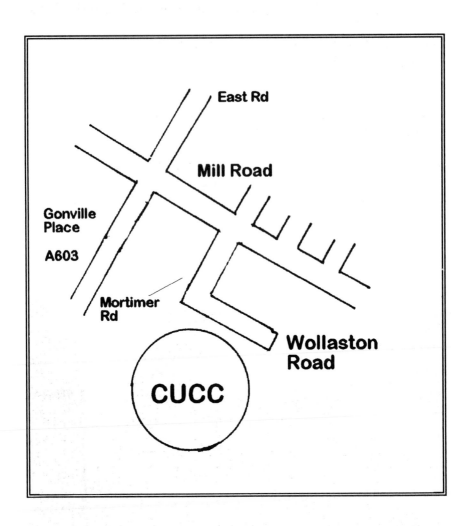

Oxford University CC

Club ground: The Parks, Parks Road, Oxford, Oxfordshire
Club address: Dr S.R. Porter, Oxford University CC, University Parks, Oxford, OX1 3RF
Telephone: 01865-557106   **Fax:** 01865-557106
Ticket Office: As above
Other telephone numbers: None

1997 Membership Subscriptions:
£10.00 per annum. No reductions given. Non members of the University welcome

Reciprocal arrangements:
None

Ground Admission:
Free

Supporters Club:
None

The Parks, Oxford (PDL)

Oxford University CC
The Parks

Description of ground: Very attractive setting in a University park. Home of Oxford University cricket - first used in 1881. Outside the city centre, the park also stages other University sports. Limited spectator facilities, but a pleasant venue for watching the students challenge the county professionals.

Address: The Parks, Parks Road, Oxford, Oxfordshire
Telephone: 01865-557106   **Capacity:** Up to 10,000

General facilities:
Club shop: No
Club museum: No
Cricket coaching facilities: No
Cricket nets: No
Other sporting or recreational
facilities on the ground: Other sports facilities in the park.
Facilities for hire or wider community use at the ground: No

Facilities and access for people with disabilities:
Wheelchair access to the ground: Yes
Designated car parking available inside the ground: Yes - contact club first
Good viewing areas inside the ground for people using wheelchairs: Yes
Designated viewing areas: No
Ramps to provide easy access to bars and refreshment outlets: Yes

Food & drink:

	Members	General Public
Full restaurant/dining facilities:	No	No
Food suitable for vegetarians:	Yes	Yes
Bars:	1	1

Travel:
Car parking: Local car parks (not very close). Street parking very restricted.
Nearest station: Oxford

Buses: City circuit electric bus, no.5. 7, 7a, 10, 25, 25a, 27, all stop at Wycliffe Hall..
Information: 01865-772250.

Tourist information: Oxford TIC,   OX1 2DA. 01865-726871.
The Old School, Gloucester Green,   Fax: 01865-240261.

Road directions:

The Parks is north of the city centre. Take the A40 (Northern by pass), and at Cutteslowe roundabout with the A4165, turn south (signposted Summertown) into Banbury Road. Turn left into Parks Road by School of Engineering, and ground is on left.

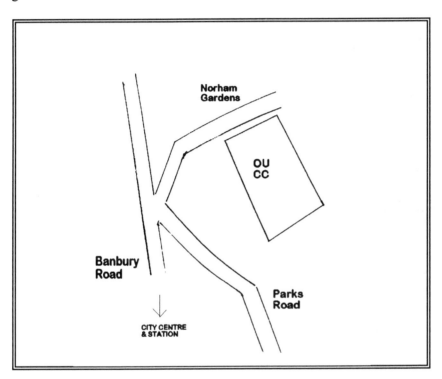

Scotland

Scottish Cricket Union
R.W. Barclay (Hon. Secretary)
Caledonia House, South Gyle, Edinburgh EH12 9DQ
Telephone: 0131-317-7247

Glasgow Titwood
Teacher's Clydesdale Cricket Club, The Pavilion, Titwood Athletic Grounds, Beaton Road, Pollokshields, Glasgow G41 4LA
Telephone: 0141-423-1463

Edinburgh
Grange Cricket Club, The Pavilion, Raeburn Place, Edinburgh EH4 1HQ
Telephone: 0131-332-2148

Forfar
Strathmore Cricket Club, The Pavilion, Lochside Park, Forfar
Telephone: 01307-464289

Ireland

Irish Cricket Union
D. Scott (Hon Secretary)
45, Foxcroft Park, Dublin 18
Telephone: 01-289-3943

Malahide
Malahide Cricket Club, Malahide, County Dublin, Ireland
Telephone: 01 8450607

Downpatrick
Downpatrick Cricket Club, Strangford Road, Downpatrick, N.Ireland
Telephone: 01396-612869

Clontarf
Clontarf Cricket Club, Castle Avenue, Dublin
Telephone: 01-833-2621

Other Cricket Organisations

Women's Cricket Association

The Association organises the Women's Cricket domestic programme and Test matches. Most of the county matches and other tournaments are played from the end of July to the beginning of September. 75 clubs affiliated for the 1996 season, playing in a regionalised National League competition, and a National Club Knockout tournament, as well as friendly matches. The 1997 season's highlight is a one day series against South Africa in August.

Associate Membership of the Association is open to all interested in women's cricket. The minimum subscription is £10.

Details of Women's Cricket fixtures and activities, and Associate Membership can be obtained from:
The Women's Cricket Association, Warwickshire County Cricket Ground, Edgbaston Road, Birmingham B5 7QX. Telephone: 0121-440-0567.

British Association for Cricketers with Disabilities

The Association promotes cricket for people with a physical disability or learning difficulty. The Association work directly with schools, colleges, Adult Education centres and through other agencies for people with disabilities. They also encourage cricket clubs to welcome people with disabilities as scorers, administrators or umpires.

The Association organises several tournaments. For further information, contact their Development Officer: *Arthur Travis, 9, Longley Walk, Chelmsley Wood, Solihull, B37 7ST. Telephone: 0121-788-2454*

County Cricket Supporters Association

The Association provides a body for supporters associations and clubs to liaise with each other, and exchange information, contact names etc. For further information, contact the Secretary, *Miss Fiona J Walker, 12, Grasmere Drive, Linton Croft, Wetherby, W.Yorkshire LS22 6GP, telephone: 01937-585179.*

MINOR
COUNTIES
NEWS

AN EXPANDED COVERAGE
FOR THE 1997 SEASON

TEN ISSUES INSTEAD OF FOUR

**Issue 1 will be a pre-season special,
and Issue 10 an end-of-season review.
Issues 2 to 9 (smaller publications)
will be published during the season.**

THE SUBSCRIPTION FOR 1997 WILL BE £10.
CHEQUES SHOULD BE MADE PAYABLE TO MIKE BERRY
AND SENT TO IDSWORTH, 3 FAIR CLOSE, FRANKTON,
NR. RUGBY, WARWICKSHIRE, CV23 9PL

WHAT THEY SAID ABOUT THE 1996 MINOR COUNTIES NEWS

"It was excellent" - Don Ambrose, Ormskirk
"A pleasure to have first hand news on the Minor Counties scene"
- Ray Groves, Lichfield
"Congratulations on a great product" - Steve Kuhlmann, Minor
Counties umpire
"Interesting and informed" - John May, Braintree
"A great publication" - Bryan Pearce, Maidstone
"A very informative read" - Barry Treadwell, Warminster

The 1997 Minor Counties Hotline 0839 44 22 20. Calls cost 50p per minute

160

Minor Counties Grounds

Minor Counties Cricket Association:
Secretary: Mr D.J.M. Armstrong
Thorpe Cottage, Mill Common, Ridlington, North Walsham
NR28 9TY.
Tel/fax: 01692-650563

Bedfordshire CCC
Contact: Mr D.J.F. Hoare
Tel: 01234-266648

Bedford Town CC
Goldington Bury,
Church Lane,
Goldington, Bedford
Tel: 01234-352458

Dunstable Town CC
Lancot Park,
Dunstable Road, Totternhoe,
Dunstable
Tel: 01582-663735

Luton Town CC
Wardown Park,
Old Bedford Road,
Luton
Tel: 01582-27855
(see page 98-99)

Henlow CC
Henlow Park, Groveside,
Henlow
Tel: 01462-811218

Southill Park CC
Southill Park Estate,
Southill
Tel: None

Berkshire CCC
Contact: Mr C.M.S. Crombie
Tel: 01734-343387 (and fax)

Falkland CC (Newbury)
Essex Street,
off Andover Road (A343),
Near Newbury
Tel: 01635-47658

Finchampstead CC
Finchampstead Park,
Reading
Tel: 01734-732890

Hurst CC
Wokingham Road,
Hurst,
Reading
Tel: 0118-9340088

Reading CC
Sonning Lane,
Reading
Tel: 01734-699049

Buckinghamshire CCC
Contact: Mr S.J.Tomlin
Tel: 01628-482202

Beaconsfield CC
Wilton Park, Oxford Road (London
side of town on A40), Beaconsfield
Old Town
Tel: 014946-674134

Aylesbury Town CC
Wendover Road, Aylesbury
Tel: 01296-415187

High Wycombe CC
London Road,
High Wycombe
Tel: 01494-522611

Marlow CC
Pound Lane, High Street,
Marlow
Tel: 016284-83638

Slough CC
Chalvey Road, Slough
Tel: 01753-520982

Cambridgeshire CCC
Contact: Mr P.W. Gooden
Tel: 01954-250429

Fenner's
(Cambridge University Ground)
Mortimer Road, Cambridge
Tel: 01223-353552
(See page 153-154)

Kimbolton School
High Street,
Kimbolton, Huntingdon, Cambs
Tel: 01480-860505

Saffron Walden CC
Anglo American Park,
Saffron Waldron, Essex
Tel: 01799-522683

Wisbech CC
Harecroft Road,
Wisbech
Tel: 01945-585429

March CC
The Avenue Sports Ground,
Burrowmoor Road, March
Tel: 01354-52029

The Leys School
Trumpington Road, Cambridge
Tel: 01223-508900

Cheshire CCC
Contact: Mr J.B. Pickup
Tel: 01606-74970

Bowdon CC
South Downs Rd, Bowdon
Tel: 0161-928-1358

Boughton Hall CC, Chester
Boughton Hall Avenue,
Filkins Lane, Chester
Tel: 01244-326072

Nantwich CC
Whitehouse Lane, Nantwich
Tel: 01270-626155

Neston CC
Parkgate, South Wirral
Tel: 0151-336-4199

New Brighton CC
Rake Lane, Wallasey
Tel: 0151-639-4900

Toft CC
Chelford Road, Knutsford
Tel: 01565-632734

Warrington CC
Walton Lea Road, Higher Walton
Warrington
Tel: 01925-263210

Cornwall CCC
Contact: Rev. Canon Ken Rogers
Tel: 01208-73867

Camborne CC
Roskear, Camborne
Tel: 01209-715478

Falmouth CC
Trescobeas, Falmouth
Tel: 01326-374000

St Austell CC
Wheal Eliza, Bethel
St Austell
Tel: 01726-72588

Truro CC
Boscawen Park, Truro
Tel: 01872-277468

Cumberland CCC
Contact: Mr D. Lamb
Tel: 01228-23017

Askam CC
James Street, Askam,
Cumbria
Tel: 01229-464576

Barrow CC
Abbey Road, Barrow, Cumbria
Tel: 01229-825201

Carlisle CC
Edenside, Carlisle, Cumbria
Tel: 01228-28593

Millom CC
St George's Road, Millom, Cumbria
Tel: 01229-772839

Netherfield CC
Parkside Road, Kendal,
Cumbria
Tel: 01539-724051

Penrith CC
Tynefield Park, Penrith,
Cumbria
Tel: 01768-863087

Devon CCC
Contact: Mr G.R.Evans
Tel: 01395-445216

Bovey Tracey CC
The Recreation Ground
Newton Road,
Bovey Tracey
Tel: 01626-832061

Budleigh Salterton CC
Ottermouth,
Budleigh Salterton
Tel: 01395-446269

Exmouth CC
The Maer Ground,
The Sea Front,
Exmouth,
Tel: 01395-272771

Torquay CC
Recreation Ground,
The Sea Front, Torquay
Tel: 01803-292001

Sidmouth CC
Fortfield Terrace,
Sidmouth
Tel: 01395-513229

North Devon CC
Sandhills, Instow
Tel: 01271-860663

United Services CC
Mount Wise, Plymouth
Tel: 01752-501548

Dorset CCC
Contact: Mr K.H. House
Tel: 01258-473394

Bournemouth CC
Dean Park,
Cavendish Road,
Bournemouth
Tel: 01202-295206

Dorchester CC
The Recreation Ground
Dorchester
Tel: 01305-263641

Sherborne School
Horsecastle, Sherborne
Tel: 01935-812431

Weymouth CC
Redlands Sports Ground
Dorchester Road,
Weymouth
Tel: 01305-813113

Herefordshire CCC
Contact: Mr P. Sykes
Tel: 01432-264703

Brockhampton CC
The Park,
Brockhampton
Tel: None

Colwall CC
Stowe Lane, Colwall
Tel: 01432-273098

Hereford City CC
Grandstand Road,
Hereford
Tel: 01432-273098

Dales CC
Mill Street, Leominster
Tel: None

Kington CC
Recreation Ground
Kington
Tel: None

Hertfordshire CCC
Contact: Mr D. Dredge
Tel: 01707-658377

Bishops Stortford CC
Cricketfield Lane,
Bishops Stortford
Tel: 01279-654463

Hertford CC
Balls Park,
Mangrove Road, Hertford
Tel: 01992-581983

Long Marston CC
Cheddington,
Long Marton
Tel: 01296-661706

Radlett CC
Cobden Hill,
Watling Street,
Radlett
Tel: 01923-856348

Shenley Cricket Centre
(The Denis Compton Ground)
Radlett Lane,
Shenley
Tel: 01923-859022

St Albans CC
Clarence Park Road, St Albans
Tel: 01727-850388

Lincolnshire CCC
Contact: Mr C.A. North
Tel: 01522-681636

Bourne CC
Abbey Lawn, Bourne
Tel: 01778-423641

Cleethorpes CC
Chichester Road, Cleethorpes
Tel: 01472-691271

Grimsby Town CC
Augusta Street,
Grimsby
Tel: 01472-360357

Grantham CC
Gorse Lane,Grantham
Tel: 01476-563742

Lincoln Lindum C.C.
St Giles Avenue,Wragby Road,
Lincoln
Tel: 01522-526592

Sleaford CC
London Road,
Sleaford
Tel: 01529-303368

Norfolk CCC
Contact: Roger Finney
Tel: 01603-477485

Lakenham Cricket Ground
Lakenham Sports & Leisure Centre
Cricket Ground Road, Norwich
Tel: 01603-477485

North Ructon CC
North Ructon
Near Kings Lynn
Tel: None

Northumberland CCC
Contact: Mr A.B.Stephenson
Tel: 0191-281-2738

County Cricket Ground
Osborne Avenue,
Jesmond, Newcastle on Tyne
Tel: 0191-281-0775

Tynemouth CC
Preston Avenue
North Shields
Tel: 0191-257-6865

Oxfordshire CCC
Contact: Mr A. Moss
Tel: 01865-372399

Rover Cowley
Roman Way Sports Ground,
Off Horspath Road,
Cowley,
Oxford
Tel: 01865-746152

Thame CC
Church Meadow, Church Road,
Thame
Tel: 01844-217799

Challow and Childrey CC
Vicarage Hill, East Challow,
Near Wantage
Tel: 01235-763335

Banbury CC
White Post Road,
Bodicote,
Banbury
Tel: 01295-264368

Aston Rowant CC
Butts Way, Kingston Blount,
Oxfordshire
Tel: None

Shropshire CCC
Contact: Mr N.H. Birch
Tel: 01743-233650

Bridgnorth CC
Victoria Road,
High Town, Bridgnorth
Tel: 01746-764919

Newport CC
Audley Avenue,
Newport
Tel: 01952-810403

Oswestry CC
Morda Road, Oswestry
Tel: 01691-653006

St George's CC
Church Road, St George's,
Telford
Tel: 01952-612911

Shrewsbury CC
London Road,
Shrewsbury
Tel: 01743-363655

Wellington CC
Orleton Park,
Wellington
Tel: 01952-251539

Shifnal CC
Priorslee Road, Shifnal
Tel: 01952-462033

Staffordshire CCC
Contact: Mr W.S. Bourne
Tel: 01902-850325

Brewood CC
Deansfield, Four Ashes Rd,
Brewood
Tel: 01902-850395

Cannock CC
The Morris Ground, Four Crosses,
Hatherton, Cannock
Tel: 01543-502424/570348

Leek CC
Highfields, Ashbourne Road,
Leek
Tel: 01538-383693

Longton CC
Trentham Road,
Blurton, Stoke on Trent
Tel: 01782-312278

Old Hill CC
Haden Park Road, Haden Hill,
Cradley Heath, Warley
Tel: 01384-566827

Stone CC
Lichfield Road, Stone
Tel: 01785-813068

Walsall CC
The Gorway,
Gorway Road, Walsall
Tel: 01922-22094

Suffolk CCC
Contact: Mr T. Pound
Tel: 01473-213288

Bury St Edmunds CC
The Victory Ground,
Nowton Road,
Bury St Edmunds
Tel: 01284-754592

Copdock & Old Ipswichians CC
Old London Road
Copdock
Tel: 01473-730752

Framlingham College
Woodbridge,
Framlingham

Ipswich School
North Field,
Ivry Street,
Ipswich
Tel: 01473-215455

Mildenhall CC
Wamil Way,
Mildenhall
Tel: 01638-712018

Ransomes/Reavell Sports Club
Sidegate Avenue,
Ipswich
Tel: 01473-726134

Wales (Minor Counties) CCC
Contact: Mr B. Edwards
Tel: 01792-462233

Colwyn Bay CC
Penryhn Avenue,
Rhos-on-Sea, Colwyn Bay
Tel: 01492-544103
(See pages 38-39)

Northop Hall CC
Smythy Lane,
Northop Hall,

Near Mold,
North Wales
Tel: 01244-810461

Panteg CC, (Newport)
Panteg, Near Newport, Gwent
Tel: 01495-756117 or
01495-755468

Penarth CC
Athletic Ground, Lavernock Road,
Penarth, South Glamorgan
Tel: 01222-708402

Pontypridd CC
Ynsyangharad Park, Pontypridd
Tel: 01443-404699 or 486542
(See pages 40-41)

Pontarddulais CC
Flosyrefail Ground,
Pontarddulais, West Glamorgan
Tel: 01792-882256

Swansea CC
St Helens Ground
Swansea
Tel: 01792-424242
(See pages 42-43)

Wiltshire CCC
Contact: Mr C.R. Sheppard
Tel: 01793-511811

Corsham CC
Station Road,
Corsham
Tel: 01249-713929

Marlborough CC
SavernakeForest,
Marlborough,
Tel: None

South Wilts CC
Bemerton Sports Ground,
Wilton Road,
Salisbury
Tel: 01722-327108

Trowbridge CC
County Ground, Timbrell Street,
Trowbridge
Tel: 01225-752538

Westbury CC
Leighton Sports Ground,
Wellhead Lane, Westbury
Tel: 01373-826438

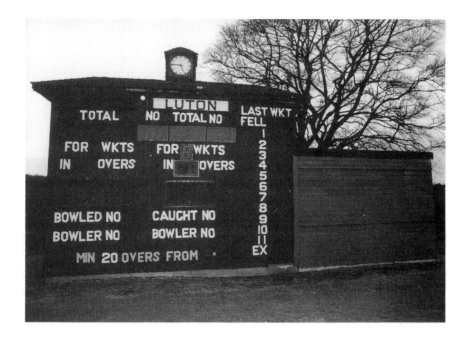

Minor Counties Cricket at Luton (PDL)

Cricket Lore

"... let me recommend to readers the quality of Cricket Lore ..."
EW Swanton - The Cricketer International

" A valuable amalgam of cricket literature and bang up to date concern and comment on the way the game is going"
David Foot- Prizewinning cricket author and journalist

" Cricket Lore, in a unique way, brings an historical perspective to contemporary issues - and vice versa"
David Rayvern Allen - Author & offcial biographer of John Arlott

"... a cricket connoisseur's delight ... Cricket Lore has the appearance and, more to the point, the substance of an enterprise of merit."
CW Porter - Journal of the Cricket Society

" the superb Cricket Lore ...." Tim Rice - The Daily Telegraph

The magazine to which these respected cricket-people refer is a limited-edition, subscription-based journal of A4 format. It is produced on quality paper to the highest possible standards of print and reproduction. The centre-fold of each issue of *Cricket Lore* features two original colour prints - removable and suitable for framing.

The magazine examines and discusses cricket's past, present and future in an informed and detailed fashion. In addition to articles on cricket's history, *Cricket Lore* also supplies considered and considerable analysis of the contemporary game and its prospects. *Cricket Lore* has published the most detailed and accurate explanation of the England Cricket Board, the most comprehensive examination of the Two-Division debate and connected issues. It has conducted surveys on ball-tampering, Wednesday starts and all the 'reform' issues. In addition to the magazine, *Cricket Lore* has also published three original books - *Mary Ann's Australians* (the first full account of the 1909 Australian tour of England), *First Knock* (a survey of opening batting partnerships) and *Darling Old Oval* (a history of 150 years of Surrey cricket at the Oval) and six facsimile editions of *James Lillywhite's Cricketers' Annual.*

A subscription is for a 10-issue volume and costs just £35.00 (post free). Volumes One and Two (issues 1-20) have been completed and the first edition of Volume Three (Issues 21-30) will be published in May. Before subscribing you may sample an Issue for just £3.50, this 'sampling cost' may be deducted from a subsequent subscription.

Cricket Lore 22 Grazebrook Road London N16 OHS Tel: 0181-800-0131

At last.
A top-class
English
cricket team.

Columns by **Matthew Engel, Scyld Berry,
Alan Lee** and **Tim de Lisle**.
Photographs by **Patrick Eagar**.
Cartoons by **Nick Newman**.
Expert tips from **Bob Woolmer**.
Jokes by **Marcus Berkmann**.
PLUS full listings of cricket on TV and radio,
a report on every Test match,
stories from all 18 counties,
pages of news, views, interviews,
nostalgia and statistics . . . and,
starting this summer: **Reality Cricket™**
the Wisden prediction competition.

The Wanderers, Johannesburg (Giles Ridley)

THE DON BRADMAN GATE

INDISPUTABLY THE WORLD'S GREATEST BATSMAN,
SIR DONALD BRADMAN MADE HIS MAIDEN
TEST MATCH HUNDRED ON THIS GROUND IN 1929 AND
THE LAST OF HIS 117 FIRST-CLASS CENTURIES HERE IN 1948.
A DEVASTATING BATSMAN CONSTANTLY ON THE ATTACK,
HE SCORED 28,067 CAREER RUNS AT 95.14 PER INNINGS
AND IN TESTS 6,996 RUNS (29 CENTURIES) AVERAGING 99.94.
WHILE SCORING THOUSANDS HE ENTERTAINED MILLIONS!

Don Bradman Gate, Mlebourne (ML)

The International Grounds

Australia:

Adelaide	178
Brisbane	180
Melbourne	181
Perth	184
Sydney	186

India:

Bangalore	190
Bombay	191
Calcutta	192
Delhi	193
Madras	194

New Zealand:

Auckland	196
Christchurch	197
Dunedin	199
Wellington	202

Pakistan:

Faisalabad	206
Karachi	206
Lahore	207
Rawalpindi	208

South Africa:

Bloemfontein	210
Cape Town	212
Durban	216
East London	217
Johannesburg	219
Port Elizabeth	222

Sri Lanka:

Colombo - R.Premadasa	226
Colombo - Sinhalese SC	227
Kandy	228

West Indies:

Bridgetown	232
Georgetown	234
Kingston	235
Kingstown	236
Port-of-Spain	237
St John's	239

Zimbabwe:

Bulawayo	241
Harare	244

Australia vs England, Sydney January 1995 (ML)

Australia vs England, Adelaide January 1995 (RO)

Australia

Grounds
Adelaide:	Adelaide Oval
Brisbane:	Brisbane Cricket Ground
Melbourne:	Melbourne Cricket Ground
Perth:	Western Australia Cricket Ground
Sydney:	Sydney Cricket Ground

Governing Body:
Australian Cricket Board
90, Jolimont Street
Jolimont
Victoria 3002
Australia
Tel: 03-654-3977
Fax: 03-654-8103

Tourist Information:
Australia Tourist Commission
10, Putney Hill
London SW1
Tel: 0990-561434(Brochure Line) or 0181-780-2227

Adelaide: Adelaide Oval

About the ground: Adelaide Oval is almost the most enduringly attractive ground in the world with St.Peter's Cathedral rising above the scoreboard and the Lofty Mountains stretching away to the north. An emigre Surrey supporter persuaded the authorities to designate the ground an Oval in 1883. The approach is through parkland with large open stands sweeping away down one side of the ground in what is a charming city on the edge of wine country. First staged test match in 1884. Regular test match venue. Home to South Australia state team.

Address: War Memorial Drive, Adelaide, South Australia,
Postal Address: Adelaide Oval, North Adelaide South Australia 5006
Telephone: 08-8300-3800   **Fax:** 08-8231-4346
Ticket Office: BASS: 08-131246 or 08-8400-2205.
Ticket information: Reductions for under 16s. Family tickets and other packages available for test matches. May be booking fee.
Capacity: 35,000

General facilities:

Cricket souvenirs shop: Yes
Cricket museum: Yes. Tours: Open to public Tuesday & Thursday mornings 10 am (unless Public Holiday or game being played). $5 adults, $2 children. Meet at South Gate. No booking required. Concludes at museum.
Other sporting or recreational facilities at the ground: Yes. SANFL football, Rugby League, concerts.

Facilities and access for people with disabilities:

Wheelchair access to the ground: Yes
Good viewing areas inside the ground for people using wheelchairs: Limited number - not many under cover.
Toilets for people with disabilities: Yes (2 at ground)

Food & drink:

Full restaurant/dining facilities: Only for members
Fast food facilities: Yes
Tea, coffee, light snacks & biscuits: Yes
Bars: For members and non members.

Travel:

Car parking: North Car Park off Pennington Tce, South Car Park off Memorial Drive
Nearest station: Adelaide (North Terrace). Information (bus & train): 08-8210 -1000.

Buses: From city centre along King William Rd
Tourist information: 08-8212-1505

Directions:

From town centre, take King William Street north from Victoria Square. This becomes King William Road. Turn left down War Memorial Drive to ground.

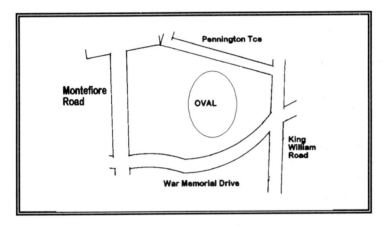

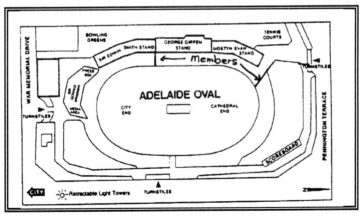

Adelaide Oval plan - courtesy of SACA inc.

Brisbane: Brisbane Cricket Ground

About the ground: The "Gabba" was first designated as a cricket ground in 1895 but did not feature a Test Match until 1931 when Australia played S.Africa. It was a bare, unattractive venue until the new grandstand complex was completed in 1975. The "Gabba" has often provided cricketing dramas particularly in the days of uncovered Pitches and unpredictable exposure to tropical thunderstorms followed by hot sunshine. The famous tied Test with the West Indies when the last four Australian batsmen were dismissed for seven runs was played on this ground. Regular test match venue. Home to Queensland State team.

Address: Brisbane Cricket Ground, Stanley Street, Wolloongabba, Brisbane, Queensland.
Postal Address: Brisbane Cricket Ground, Gabba Towers, 411 Vulture Street, Quensland 4169
Telephone: 07-3891-5464   **Fax:** 07-3393-0298

Travel:
Nearest station: Vulture St   07-131230
Buses: Information buses & trains: *Tourist information:* 07-3221-8411.

Directions:
Riverside Expressway (Metroad 3) south from city centre. Cross Brisbane River, and take turning for Vulture Street. Ground is on right.

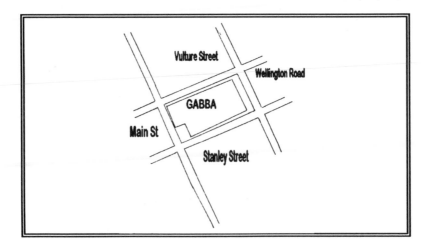

Melbourne: Melbourne Cricket Ground

About the ground: The MCG is the world's largest cricket ground, was the venue for the 1956 Olympic Games and hosts crowds of 100.000 for the finals of Australian Rules football. The club was founded in the 1830's. Although flower beds and shrubs have given way to large concrete stands, the approach is through attractive parkland. The first English team to play in Australia in 1862 planted trees in Yarra Park with the first test match played at Melbourne in 1877; Australia won by 45 runs !! Home of the Melbourne CC, founded in 1838.

Address: Yarra Park, Jolimont Terrace, Jolimont, East Melbourne, Victoria
Postal Address: P.O. Box 175, East Melbourne 3002, Victoria.
Telephone: 03- 9657-8888   **Fax:** 03-9650-5682
Ticket Office: Contact BASS (ticket agency): 03-11500, enquiries: 11566
Capacity: 100,000

General facilities:
Cricket souvenirs shop: Yes
Cricket museum: Australian Gallery of Sport & Olympic Museum 03- 654-8922. Australian Cricket Hall of Fame, Melbourne CC museum. Tours of MCG available -03-654-8922.
Other sporting or recreational facilities at the ground: Australian rules football, concerts

Facilities and access for people with disabilities:
Wheelchair access to the ground: Yes
Good viewing areas inside the ground for people using wheelchairs: Yes - under cover level 2 Great Southern stand
Toilets for people with disabilities: Yes

Food & drink:
Full restaurant/dining facilities: Members only
Fast food facilities: Yes
Tea, coffee, light snacks & biscuits: Yes
Bars: Ample

Travel:
Car parking: Yarra Park, immediately by ground.
Nearest station: Jolimont or Richmond
Buses: Information buses & trains: 03-131638
Tourist information: 03-9653-9777

181

Directions:

From city centre, take Flinders Street east, and turn into Wellington Parade. Turn right into Brunton Ave, and ground on left.

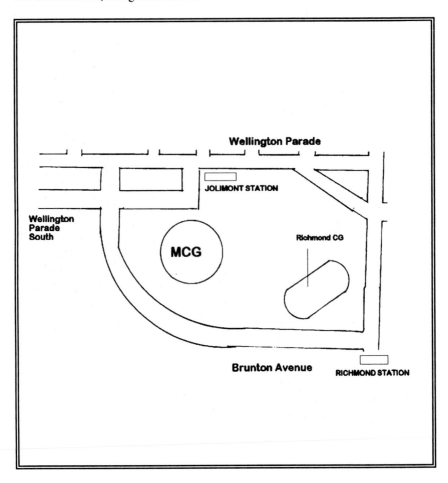

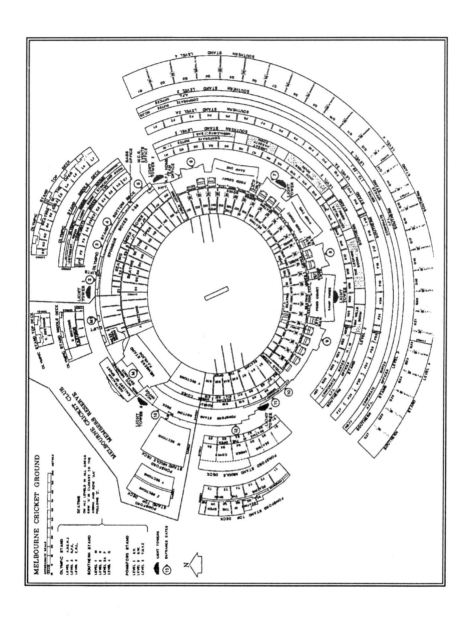

Melbourne Cricket Ground plan - courtesy of Melbourne Cricket Club

Perth: Western Australia Cricket Association Cricket Ground

About the ground: The "WACA" is a well appointed spacious Test Match ground approached through the park from the city centre and attractively different from the large, grandstand dominated grounds of the Eastern States. The "WACA" did not feature a Test Match until Australia v England in 1970 but is now an established, well appointed venue by the Swan River in a vibrant, modern city.

Address: Nelson Crescent, East Perth,6004, Western Australia
Postal Address: PO Box 6045, East Perth WA 6892
Telephone: 09-265-7222   **Fax:** 09-221-1823
Ticket Office: Red Tickets 09-484-1222
Ticket information: Tickets available from Red Ticket outlets. Adult Test match prices (1996-7) $17 to $30. Reductions for senior citizens, students and children. Also family tickets. Multi day passes and match passes available
Capacity: 28,500 for cricket.

General facilities:

Cricket souvenirs shop: Yes
Cricket museum: Yes
Other sporting or recreational facilities at the ground: Aussie rules football, and many other sports. Concerts. Function rooms available.

Facilities and access for people with disabilities:

Wheelchair access to the ground: Yes
Good viewing areas inside the ground for people using wheelchairs: Yes. Outside under cover on flat surface, or internal air conditioned smoke free bars.
Toilets for people with disabilities: Yes

Food & drink:

Full restaurant/dining facilities: Yes. Extensive marquee/hospitality facilities for major international matches
Fast food facilities: Yes
Tea, coffee, light snacks & biscuits: Yes

Travel:

Car parking: None inside ground. 10 public car parks nearby.
Nearest station: Claisebrook
*Buses:*Information buses & trains: 09-132213
Tourist information: 09-483-1111

Directions:

Ground is east of town centre. Nelson Crescent is off Hay Street, which goes straight there from Victoria Square. Hay Street is a main thoroughfare, and leads directly to the ground. Part of it is one way going towards the city centre.

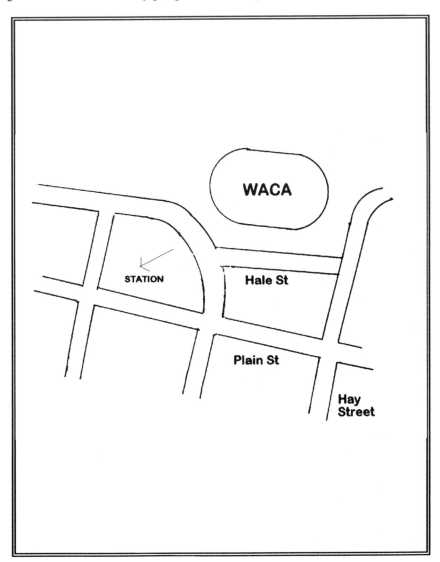

Sydney: Sydney Cricket Ground

About the ground: A spectacular modern sports stadium featuring Rugby League, Australian Rules and international athletics. The Bradman and Noble stands and hospitality suites provide a high standard of modern seating accommodation. With turrets and pinnacles to the right of the pavilion, the whole arena retains its style and sense of history and great events in the game. First test match in February 1882.

Address: Moore Park Road, Paddington, Sydney, NSW
Postal Address: GPO Box 150, Sydney, NSW 2001
Telephone: 02-9360-6601. Customer service: 02-380-0318
Fax:02-9360-1319
Ticket Office: Contact Ticketek 02-9266-4800. Fax: 02-9260-0261
Ticket information: Test match tickets $20-$35. Concessions available.
Capacity: 41,006

General facilities:
Cricket souvenirs shop: Yes
Cricket museum: Yes - part of Sportspace interactive sports adventure tour: 02-380-0383
Also (not at stadium): Bradman museum: PO Box 999, St Jude Street, Bowral NSW 2576. Tel: 048-621247.Fax:048-612536
Other sporting or recreational facilities at the ground: Aussie rules & concerts at SCG. Soccer, Rugby League & Rugby Union at adjoining Football Stadium.

Facilities and access for people with disabilities:
Wheelchair access to the ground: Yes
Designated car parking available inside the ground: Yes - near Properties & Services office.
Good viewing areas inside the ground for people using wheelchairs: Yes - top deck of Brewongle stand
Toilets for people with disabilities: Yes

Food & drink:
Full restaurant/dining facilities: Yes
Fast food facilities: Yes
Tea, coffee, light snacks & biscuits: Yes
Bars: Yes

Travel:

Car parking: Moore Park car park (opposite SCG) for public
Nearest station: Bus from Central station. Information for buses & trains: 02-131500

Buses: 339, 372, 374, 376, 393, 395.
Tourist information: 02-9224-4442

Directions:

In Paddington area of city. Take Oxford Street from Hyde Park. Turn into Oatley Road, and Football Stadium is at end of road. Turn right into Moore Park Road, and left into Driver Avenue. SCG is on left, parking on right.

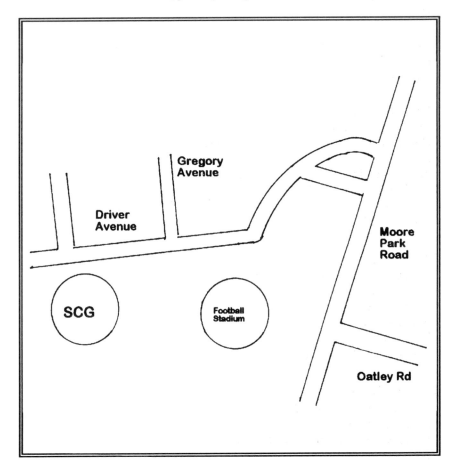

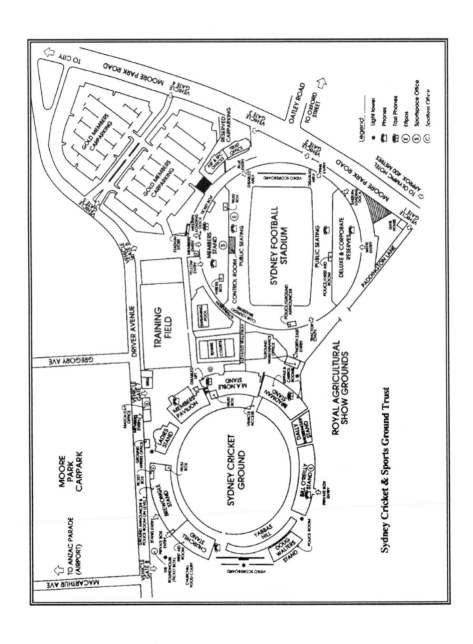

Plan of Sydney Cricket Ground - courtesy Sydney Cricket & Sports Ground Trust

188

India

Grounds

Bangalore:	**M. Chinnaswamy Cricket Stadium**
Bombay:	**Wankede Stadium**
Calcutta:	**Eden Gardens**
Delhi:	**Feroz Shah Kotla**
Madras:	**M. A.Chidamabaram Stadium**

Governing Body:
The Board of Control for Cricket in India
Dr B.C. Roy Club House
Eden Gardens
Calcutta 700 021
India
Tel: 033-2481715 or 033-483414 or 033-483191
Fax: 033-2487555

Tourist Information:
India Government Tourist Office
7 Cork St
London W1
0171-437-3677
0181-812-0929

Bangalore: M. Chinnaswamy Stadium

About the ground: First Test match in 1974 against the West Indies. Has staged 10 Test matches.

Address: Mahatma Gandhi Road, Bangalore, Karanataka State
Postal Address: Karnataka State Cricket Association, M. Chinnaswamy Stadium Mahatma Gandhi Road, Bangalore, Karnataka State 560 001
Telephone: 080-564487/5543490   **Fax:** 080-5543490
Capacity: 50,000

Travel:
*Nearest station:*Bangalore
Contonment or City station

Buses: City bus stand 0.75 miles
Tourist information: 80-579517

Directions:
Near city centre, next to Cubbon Park. From town hall, take Wodeyar Road towards the park. This becomes Kasturba Road, and then Mahatma Gandhi Road. Ground on left at end of park.

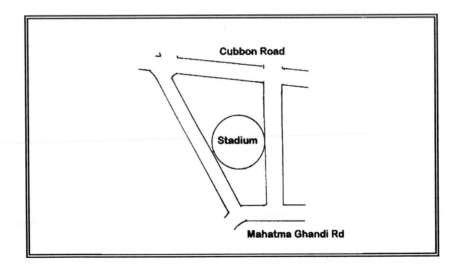

Bombay: Wankede Stadium

About the ground: Bombay is the cricket capital of India. First used for Test cricket in 1975. Replaced the nearby Brabourne Stadium as Bombay's Test match venue. Clive Lloyd scored 242 in the first Test match. Some stands named after famous Indian cricketers, including Merchant and Gavaskar.

Address: "D" Road, Churchage, Bombay , Maharashtra,
Postal Address: Bombay Cricket Association, "D" Road, Churchage, Bombay , 400 020 , Maharashtra,
Telephone: 022-2863463 / 2863464 / 2863455   **Fax:** None
Capacity: 45,000

Travel:
Nearest station: Churchgate   *Tourist information:* 022-202-6713

Directions:
From Horniman Circle, take Veer Nariman Road towards Back Bay. After second roundabout, turn right onto E Road South,then left onto D Road. Stadium on right.

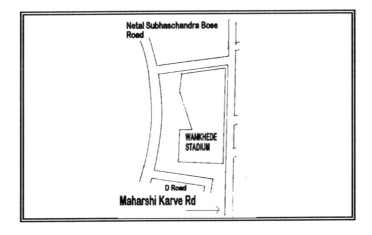

Calcutta: Eden Gardens

About the ground: First used in 1864 by the Calcutta Cricket Club. The Pavilion was built in 1871. The second ground to stage a Test match in India, in 1934. The first, the Gymkhana Ground in Bombay is no longer used for first class cricket, making Eden Gardens the oldest Test venue still in use, and the oldest ground in India.

Address: Strand Road South, Calcutta, West Bengal
Postal Address: Cricket Association of Bengal, Dr B.C. Roy Club House, Eden Gardens, Calcutta 700 021
Telephone: 033-282447/280411 **Fax:** 033-2487555
Capacity: 100,000

Travel:
Nearest station: Sealdah *Tourist information:* 033-288271

Directions:
Eden Gardens is on the south bank of the Hooghly river. It is next to Fort William, and a couple of blocks from the General Post Office. From Bose Road, take Lenin Sarahi towards the Ochterlony Monument, and the ground is across Red Road.

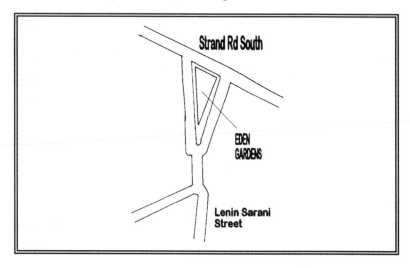

Delhi: Feroz Shah Kotla Grounds

About the ground: Built in 1883, on behalf of a few local people and princes of state. First staged a Test match in 1948, against the West Indies.

Address: Bahadurshah Zafar Marg, New Delhi,
Postal Address: Delhi & District Cricket Association, Feroz Shah Kotla Grounds, Bahadurshah Zafar Marg, New Delhi, 110 002
Telephone: 011-3319683 or 3319323   **Fax:** None
Capacity: 30,000

Travel:
Nearest station: New Delhi   *Tourist information:* 011-3313637

Directions:
From New Delhi station, take Jawaharlal Nehru Marg towards Yamuna river. Turn right into Bahadurshah Zafar Marg for ground.

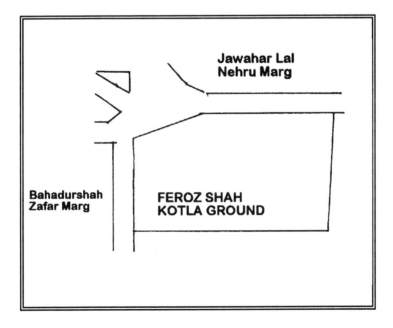

Madras: M. A.Chidamabaram Stadium

About the ground: Cricket has been played here since 1865. Pavilion built in 1892. Now leased by Tamil Nadu Cricket Association. First Test match in 1934. Usually referred to as Chepauk stadium. Very beautiful location. Test matches often coincide with the Pongal festival - a three day holiday. India's tied Test with Australia was played here, and Sri Lanka played their first Test match here.

Address: Victoria Hostel Road, Chepauk, Madras
Postal Address: Victoria Hostel Road, Chepauk, Madras, 600 005
Telephone: 044-844175 or 044-840096   **Fax:** None
Capacity: 55,000

Travel:

Nearest station: Egmore or Park, both   044-563351
1.5 miles from ground. Information: *Tourist information:* 044-561982

Directions:

To north east of city centre. Take Anna Salai north, turn right into Wallajah Road, and stadium on right.

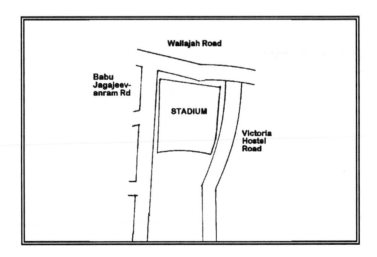

New Zealand

Grounds:

Auckland:	Eden Park
Christchurch:	Lancaster Park
Dunedin:	Carisbrook Cricket Ground
Wellington:	Basin Reserve

Governing Body:
New Zealand Cricket (Inc.)
PO Box 958
109, Cambridge Terrace
Christchurch
Tel: 03-366-2964
Fax: 03-365-7491

Tourist information:
NZ High Commission
80 Haymarket
SW1Y 4TQ
Fax: 0171-839-8929

Auckland: Eden Park

About the ground: Eden Park was substantially improved for the 1992 World Cup. The West Stand was completed with two tiered seating in line with the pitch which is unusually on the diagonal. The ground is about five miles from the city centre. England dismissed New Zealand for 26 on this ground in 1955, their lowest Test match score!! First staged Test match in 1930. Regular Test match venue.

Address: Reimers Avenue, Auckland
Postal Address: Eden Park Trust Broad, Reimers Avenue, Mount Eden, Auckland
Telephone: 09-849-5555   **Fax:** 09-815-0138
Ticket Office: 09-849-5100

Travel:

Nearest station: Auckland. Information:0800-802 802

Buses: Information:09-366-6400
Tourist information: 09-366-6888

Directions:

From city centre, take Dominion Road towards Balmoral area. Turn right into Bellwood Avenue, and ground at end of road.

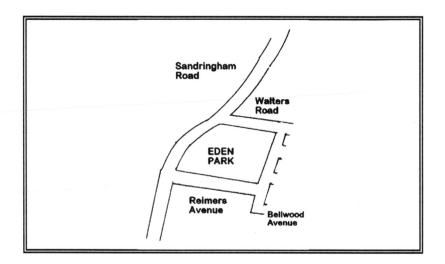

196

Christchurch: Lancaster Park

About the ground: First ground to stage a Test match in New Zealand, against England in 1930. The South Island landscape is rugged and dominated by the Alps which provide an attractive context for the ground. The venue has been upgraded and the new Hadlee Stand is an impressive facility with a viewing gallery, hospitality areas and public seating. In the 1978 Test Botham ran out Boycott and in 1984 New Zealand beat England by an innings and 132 runs in just over 22 hours of play!

Address: Wilsons Road, Christchurch,
Postal Address: PO Box 10196, Christchurch
Telephone: 03-379-1765   **Fax:** 03-366-1115
Ticket Office: Ticketek: 03-377-8899
Ticket information: Test matches: contact Ticketek for details
Capacity: 25,000

General facilities:
Cricket souvenirs shop: Yes   Rugby League, concerts.
Cricket museum: Yes
Other sporting or recreational facilities at the ground: Rugby Union,

Facilities and access for people with disabilities:
Wheelchair access to the ground: Yes
Good viewing areas inside the ground for people using wheelchairs: Yes - can hold 25 - 30.
Toilets for people with disabilities: Yes

Food & drink:
Full restaurant/dining facilities: No
Fast food facilities: Yes
Tea, coffee, light snacks & biscuits: Yes

Travel:
Car parking: At ground only for members & season ticket holders. Street parking available

Nearest station: Christchurch
Buses: Information: 03-366-8855
Tourist information: 03-379-9629

Directions:

From city centre, take Moorhouse Avenue towards Phillipstown. Turn right into Falsgrave Street, and left into Stevens Street. Ground on right.

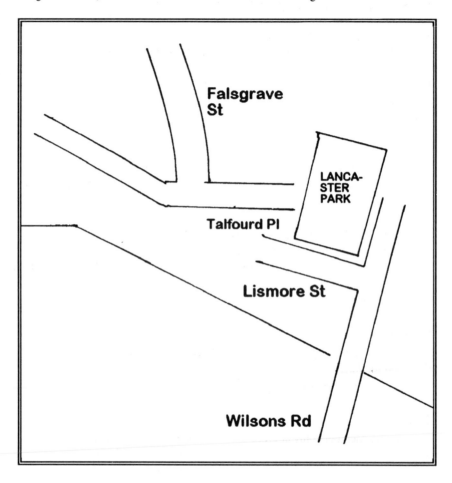

Dunedin: Carisbrook Cricket Ground

About the ground: First staged test match in 1955, against England.

Address: Burns Street, Dunedin
Postal Address: Otago Cricket Association, PO Box 1419, Dunedin
Telephone: 03-455-4056   **Fax:** 03-455-4250
Ticket Office: Test match tickets from Ticketer offices
Ticket information: As above
Capacity: 22,000

General facilities:
Cricket souvenirs shop: Yes
Cricket museum: No

Other sporting or recreational facilities at the ground: Rugby Union

Facilities and access for people with disabilities:
Wheelchair access to the ground: Yes
Good viewing areas inside the ground for people using wheelchairs: Yes - in front of main stand.
Toilets for people with disabilities: Yes

Food & drink:
Full restaurant/dining facilities: No (Corporate hospitality only)
Fast food facilities: Yes
Tea, coffee, light snacks & biscuits: Yes

Travel:
Car parking: Members only at ground. Street parking or local car parks available.

Nearest station: Dunedin
Buses: Contact visitor centre.
Tourist information: 03-474-3300

Directions:

From town centre, take Princes St towards Kensington. Fork right into South Road, and left into Burns Street to ground.

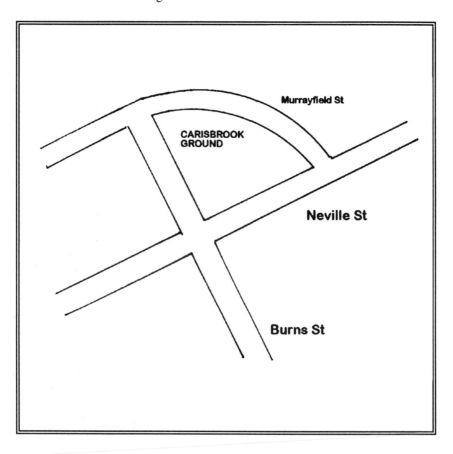

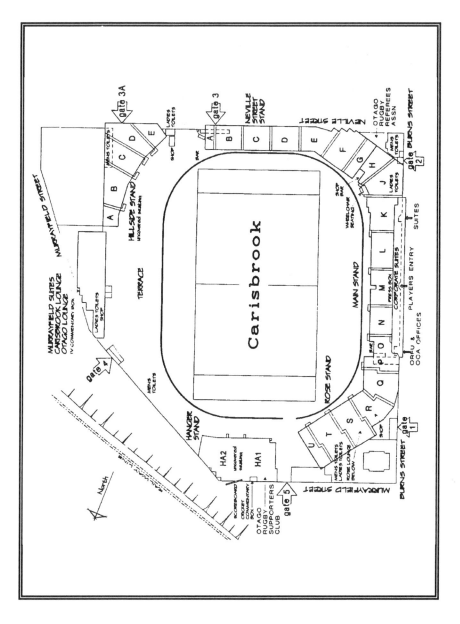

Carisbrook Plan - courtesy Otago Cricket Assocation (Inc)

Wellington: Basin Reserve

About the ground: First staged test cricket in 1930. The Basin Reserve is the country's oldest Test ground; originally a lake and then a swamp after the Te Aro earthquake. A traditional cricket ground, viewing from the hillside; redeveloped in the early 1980's. There are plans for a multi-complex stadium.

Address: Sussex Street, Wellington
Postal Address: Sussex Street, Wellington
Telephone: 04-384-5227   **Fax:** None
Ticket Office: 04-384-3171
Ticket information: Test match tickets from Bass Ticketek
Capacity: 12,500

General facilities:
Cricket souvenirs shop: No
Cricket museum: Yes
Other sporting or recreational facilities at the ground: Yes. Soccer, rugby, american football, operas & concerts.

Facilities and access for people with disabilities:
Wheelchair access to the ground: Yes
Good viewing areas inside the ground for people using wheelchairs: Yes
Toilets for people with disabilities: Yes

Food & drink:
Full restaurant/dining facilities: Yes
Fast food facilities: Yes
Tea, coffee, light snacks & biscuits: Yes

Travel:
Car parking: Very limited at ground. Street parking.
Nearest station: Wellington.
Information: 04-472-5399
Buses: Information: 04-385-9955
Tourist information: 04-801-4000

Directions:
From Wellington Harbour, Kent Terrace leads directly to the ground.

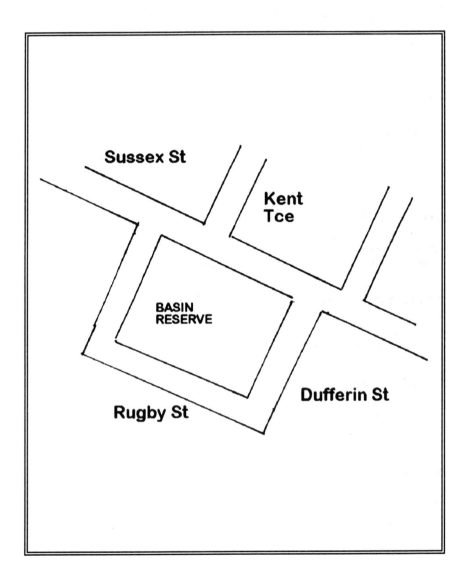

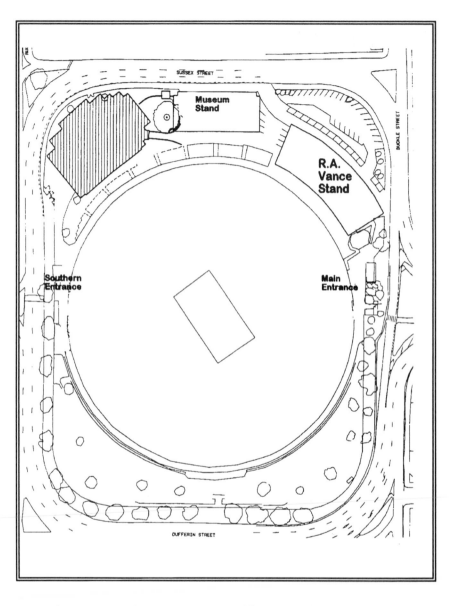

Basin Reserve Plan - courtesy Wellington Cricket Association

Pakistan

Grounds:
Faisalabad: Iqbal Stadium
Karachi: National Cricket Stadium
Lahore: Gadaffi Stadium
Rawalpindi: Rawalpindi Cricket Stadium

Governing Body:
Pakistan Cricket Board
Gaddafi Stadium
Lahore 54600
Pakistan
Tel: 042-5759936 or 042-877817
Fax: 042-571-1860

Tourist Information:
High Commission for Pakistan
35, Lowndes Square
London SW1
Tel: 0171-235-2044
There is no tourist office.

Facilities:

We have been told by a Pakistan Cricket follower via the Internet that all the Grounds featured here provide tea, coffee, cold drinks, fast food and light snacks.

Faisalabad: Iqbal Cricket Stadium

About the ground: Pakistan's main industrial city. First Test match in 1978. Stadium first used in 1966-7 season.

Address: Iqbal Cricket Stadium, Faisalabad.
Telephone: 0411-30156   **Fax:** None

Travel:
Station: Faisalabad   *Tourist information:* 0411-612375

Karachi: National Cricket Stadium

About the ground: Karachi is the city of beautiful beaches and unbelievable heat in the summer. The stadium has been renovated. First Test match in 1955 against India.

Address: 12, Stadium Road, Karachi
Telephone: 021-4963740   **Fax:** 021-4981217
Capacity: 50,000

Travel:
Tourist information: 021-511293

Directions:
The stadium is north east of the city centre. Take MA Jinnah Road, this leads into University Road, and Stadium Road is turning on right.

Lahore: Gaddafi Cricket Stadium

About the ground: Lahore was the centre of the Mughal Empire and gardens, mosques and forts are an outstanding feature of Mughal architecture in this great city. The Ground was a building site when the England 'A' Team visited in November 1995, but refurbished for the 1996 World Cup with substantial facilities, hospitality areas and floodlights for night games. First Test match in 1959. Staged 1996 World Cup Final.

Address: Ferozepur Road, Lahore
Telephone: 042-5754737 or 042-5763158 **Fax:** 042-5711860
Capacity: 60,000

Travel:
Nearest station: Lahore City. Local   *Tourist information:* 042-303624
stations: Mian Mir or Walton

Directions:
From Old City area, Ferozepur Road leads directly to the stadium.

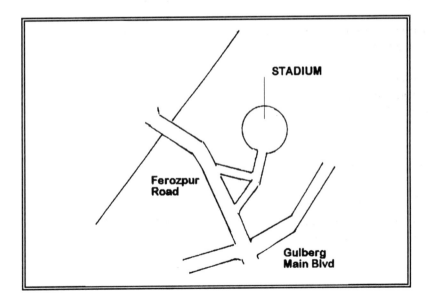

207

Rawalpindi: Rawalpindi Cricket Stadium

About the ground: Also known as the Qamar Ahmed Stadium. The latest addition to Test centres in Pakistan, the ground is a very attractive 30,000 capacity stadium with a backdrop of the Margalla Hills. First Test match against Zimbabwe in 1993. Has replaced the Pindi Club Ground as the Test venue for the City.

Address: Rawalpindi Cricket Stadium,Rawalpindi
Telephone: 051-424717 or 051-423677   **Fax:** None
Capacity: 30,000

Travel:
Station: Rawlpindi City Station,   *Tourist information:* 051-581480
or local stations.

Directions:
On the edge of the city, three miles from Islamabad.

Village cricket in Pakistan (RO)

South Africa

Grounds:
Bloemfontein: Springbok Park
Cape Town: Newlands
Centurion: Centurion Park
Durban: Kingsmead
East London: Buffalo Park
Johannesburg: Wanderers
Port Elizabeth: St George's Park

Governing Body:
United Cricket Board of South Africa
P.O. Box 55009
Northlands 2116
South Africa
Tel: 011-880-2810
Fax: 011-880-6578

Tourist information:
The South African Tourism Board
5, Alt Grove
London SW19
Tel: 0181-944-6646

Bloemfontein: Springbok Park

About the ground: Stages one day internationals. Home of Free State team.

Address: Att Horak Street, Bloemfontein, Free State
Postal Address: P. O. Box 4357, Bloemfontein 9300, Free State
Telephone: 051-447-5715
Fax: 051-447-2208
Ticket Office: 051-430-6365
Ticket information: Test match & one day international tickets available from club.
Reserved: R65, unreserved: adults R45, scholars: R30 (maximum 4,000)

General facilities:
Cricket souveniers shop: Yes
Cricket museum: No
Other sporting or recreational facilities at the ground: Football, concerts, church services.
Kiddies play corner at ground at Loch Logan End.

Facilities and access for people with disabilities:
Wheelchair access to the ground: Yes
Good viewing areas inside the ground for people using wheelchairs: Yes - under cover next to main stand
Toilets for people with disabilities: Yes

Food & drink:
Full restaurant/dining facilities: No
Fast food facilities: Yes
Tea, coffee, light snacks & biscuits: Yes
Bars: 5 public and 1 members

Travel:
Car parking: Plenty within 0.75 miles of ground.
Nearest station: Bloemfontein
Buses: Information: 051-405-8135
Tourist information: 051-405-8490, Hoffman Sq.

Directions:

From N1, take R64 towards city centre. Turn right into Erstelaan, and right into Kingsway. Ground is on left.

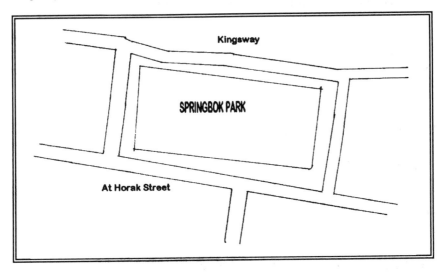

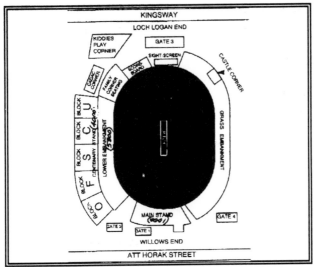

Springbok Park plan - courtesy Free State Cricket Union

Cape Town: Newlands Cricket Ground

About the ground: First staged test cricket in 1889. Regular test match venue. Home of Western Province Cricket Club. Modern ground with floodlights and electronic scoreboards. The modern Newlands ground is still dominated by Table Mountain but much changed in recent years. Substantial gound developments particularly in corporate facilities, and a new stand where the famous oaks once grew.

Address: 146, Camp Ground Road, Newlands 7700, Cape Town, South Africa
Postal Address: As above.
Telephone: 021-615120   **Fax:** 021-683-2322
Ticket Office: Computicket outlets
Ticket information: Test matches: R20 per day. Day/night internationals: R50 or R75 (depends on opposition)
Reciprocal arrangement with Surrey CCC and the Cricketers' Club of London

General facilities:
Cricket souveniers shop: Yes
Cricket museum: No
Other sporting or recreational facilities at the ground: Squash and tennis courts for club members.

Facilities and access for people with disabilities:
Wheelchair access to the ground: Yes
Good viewing areas inside the ground for people using wheelchairs: Yes
Toilets for people with disabilities: Yes

Food & drink:
Full restaurant/dining facilities: No
Fast food facilities: Yes
Tea, coffee, light snacks & biscuits: Yes
Bars: At least four

Travel:
Car parking: School fields within 5 minute walk.
Nearest station: Newlands. Information: 021-405-2991
Buses: Information: 021-934-0540
Tourist information: Tourist Rendezvous (at Cape Town station): 021-418-5202

Directions:

From city centre, take N2 or M3. Exit freeway at Rondebosch/Rhodes Memorial keeping left into Princess Anne Avenue and Klipper Road Turn right onto Main Road (M4), and left into Camp Ground. Ground is on left.

Alternative route: From city centre, stay on N2. Exit the N2 at junction with Liesbeek Parkway. Turn right onto Liesbeek Parkway; stay on this road, which becomes Camp Ground. At junction with Palmyra Road, follow Camp Ground to right, and ground is on right. (Parking on school field opposite Ground)

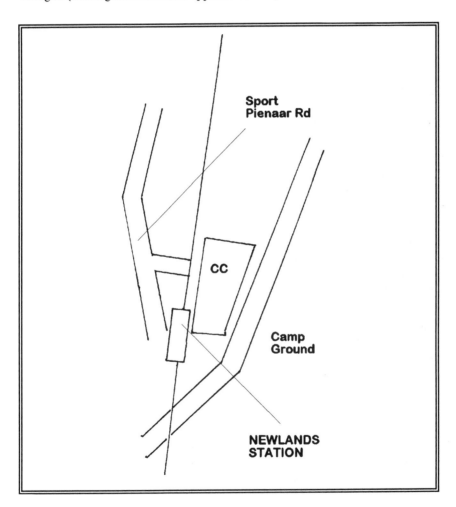

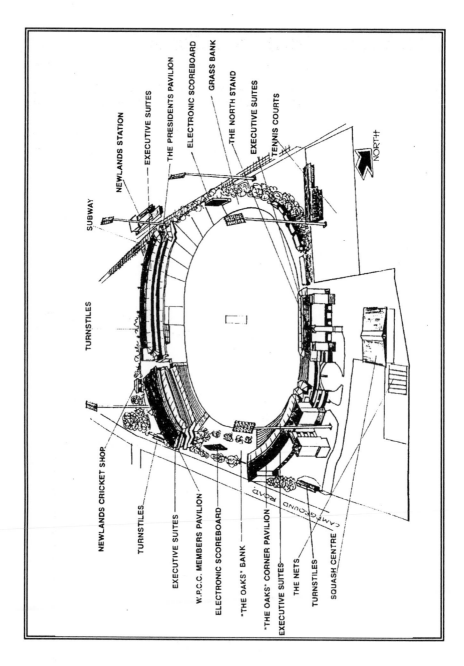

NORTH

GRASS BANK

ELECTRONIC SCOREBOARD

THE PRESIDENTS PAVILION

EXECUTIVE SUITES

NEWLANDS STATION

THE NORTH STAND

EXECUTIVE SUITES

TENNIS COURTS

SUBWAY

TURNSTILES

NEWLANDS CRICKET SHOP

TURNSTILES

EXECUTIVE SUITES

W.P.C.C. MEMBERS PAVILION

ELECTRONIC SCOREBOARD

"THE OAKS" BANK

"THE OAKS" CORNER PAVILION

EXECUTIVE SUITES

THE NETS

TURNSTILES

SQUASH CENTRE

CAMP GROUND ROAD

Newlands plan - courtesy Western Province Cricket Club

Centurion: Centurion Park

About the ground: Hosted its first Test Match aginst England in November 1995 but a combination of African thunderstorm and English rain literally washed the game out after two days One main stand, open terracing and sun shades and deck chairs on one side mean very exposed cricket watching when the sun does shine! Headquarters of Northern Transvaal Cricket Union. In suburb of Centurion (formerly Verwoerdburg), south of Pretoria.

Address: Centurion Park, Lenchen South, Centurion, Gauteng
Postal Address: Northern Transvaal CU, PO Box 7706, Hennopsmeer 0046
Telephone: 012-663-1005
Fax: 012-663-3329
Ticket Office: As above

Travel:

Nearest station: Suburban service. Information: 012-315-2007

Buses: Information: 012-313-0839
Tourist information: 012-323-1222

Directions:

From N1 junction with John Vorster Drive, head towards town centre. Turn right into Lenchen South, and ground is on right.

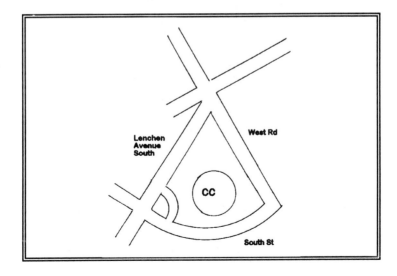

Durban: Kingsmead

About the ground: First staged test cricket in 1923. Home of Natal Cricket Union. Staged the "timeless test" in 1938-9.

Address: Old Fort Road, Durban, Natal.
Postal Address: Natal Cricket Union, PO Box 47266, Greyville 4023
Telephone: 031-32-9703
Fax: 031-32-5288
Ticket Office: As above

Travel:

Car parking: Local car parks
Nearest station: Durban (0.5 miles)
Information: 031-361-7652

Buses: Information: 031-307-3505
Tourist information: 031-304-4934

Directions:

Ground is in the cenetre of town, at the junction of the M12 (N.M.R. Avenue) and the M4 (Old Fort)

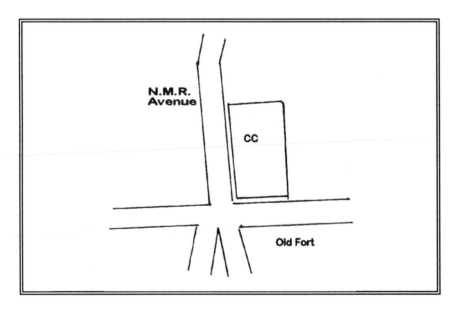

East London: Buffalo Park

About the ground: Used for one day internationals, not test matches. Home of Border team.

Address: Buffalo Park, Buffalo Park, East London
Postal Address: P.O. Box 803, East London, 5200.
Telephone: 0431-437757
Fax: 0431-433293
Ticket Office: As above.
Ticket information: As above. Contact Mrs Diane Sime.
Capacity: 17,000

General facilities:
Cricket souveniers shop: Yes
Cricket museum: No
Other sporting or recreational

facilities at the ground: Rugby and hockey.

Facilities and access for people with disabilities:
Wheelchair access to the ground: Yes
Designated car parking available inside the ground: Yes - contact club first.
Good viewing areas inside the ground for people using wheelchairs: Yes
Toilets for people with disabilities: No

Food & drink:
Full restaurant/dining facilities: No
Tea, coffee, light snacks & biscuits: Yes
Bars: Castle Corner. Castle Supporters Club: reserved seats, bar & fast food.
Fast food facilities: Yes

Travel:
Car parking: Members only at ground. Street parking, and at Marina Glen when available.
Nearest station: East London

(1 mile)
Buses: None to ground - use private taxis. 0431-21251.
Tourist information: 0431-26015

217

Directions:

From town centre, take M6 (Fleet St)- (leads to M4). Turn left into Fitzpatrick St - still M6. Stay on this road which becomes the R102. Turn right into Buffalo Park, and ground is on left.

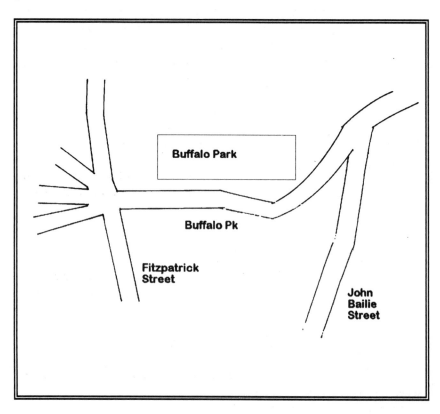

Johannesburg: Wanderers Stadium

About the ground: The Wanderers is one of the most famous clubs in the world. The Old Wanderers ground first staged test cricket in 1896, and is now the site of the Johannesburg railway station. This ground first used for test cricket in 1956. Home of Transvaal team. The Wanderers Stadium is both the newest and largest ground in S.Africa. Major modernisation programme since 1991, including work on the stands, new floodlights and a giant video screen.

Address: Corlett Drive, Illovo, Johannesburg, Gauteng
Postal Address: Transvaal Cricket Board, PO Box 55309, Northlands 2116
Telephone: 011-788-1008   **Fax:** 011-880-6229
Ticket Office: As above. Extension 218
Ticket information: Tickets available from ground, or from Computicket. 5- day packs available for Test matches. Some reductions for school students and senior citizens.
Capacity: 30,000 plus 175 corporate suites

General facilities:
Cricket souveniers shop: Yes
Cricket museum: Yes
Other sporting or recreational facilities at the ground: Not at present. Other sports facilities nearby.

Facilities and access for people with disabilities:
Wheelchair access to the ground: Yes
Good viewing areas inside the ground for people using wheelchairs: Yes. Behind first tier of grandstand seating in Centenary stand.
Toilets for people with disabilities: Yes

Food & drink:
Full restaurant/dining facilities: Yes (VIP guests only)
Fast food facilities: Yes
Tea, coffee, light snacks & biscuits: Yes

Travel:
Car parking: Street parking. Rugby fields by stadium (not public). Park and ride scheme for Test matches and one day internationals
Nearest station: Johannesburg - 4 miles (No suburban services)

Information: 011-773-5878   *Tourist information:* 011-336-4961
Buses: Information: 011-838-2125

Directions: Take N1 north from city centre. Turn left into Corlett Drive (M30), and ground is right, around 1 mile from motorway junction.

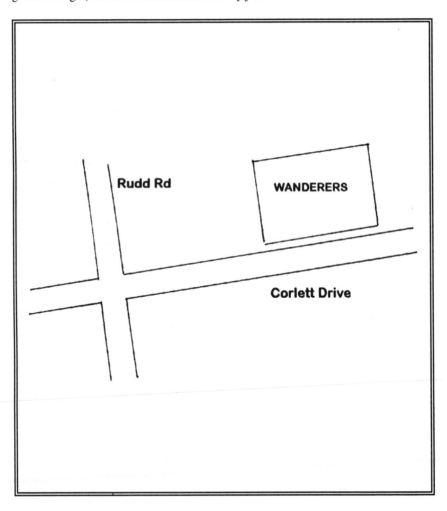

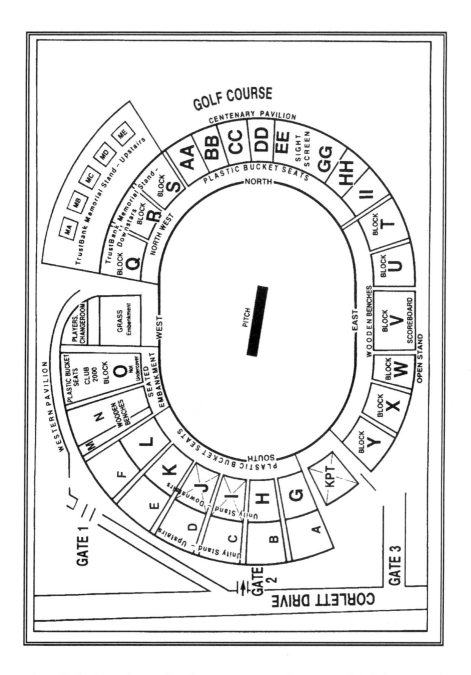

Plan of The Wanderers Stadium - courtesy of Transvaal Cricket Board

Port Elizabeth: St Georges Park

About the ground: First staged a Test match in 1889, against England the first ground to do so outside England or Australia. Home of Eastern Province team. The club was formed in 1843. Most of the accommodation is in one spacious stand.

Address: Park Drive, Port Elizabeth, Eastern Cape.
Postal address: P.O. Box 12327, Centrahill 6006
Telephone: 041-551646
Fax: 041-564259
Ticket Office: As above
Ticket information: Contact club for test match & one day internationals.
Capacity: 17,500

General facilities:
Cricket souveniers shop: Yes
Cricket museum: No
Other sporting or recreational facilities at the ground: Rugby, hockey, squash, concerts. Facilities also for weddings, parties etc.

Facilities and access for people with disabilities:
Wheelchair access to the ground: Yes
Designated car parking available inside the ground: Contact club
Good viewing areas inside the ground for people using wheelchairs: Yes
Toilets for people with disabilities: Yes
All facilities for the disabled are in the Duckpond pavilion.

Food & drink:
Full restaurant/dining facilities: No
Fast food facilities: Yes
Tea, coffee, light snacks & biscuits: Yes

Travel:
Car parking: Union field & "B" field members only. Street parking, and at Greenwood school.
Nearest station: Port Elizabeth (less than 1 mile).
Information: 041-507-2400
Buses: In city centre.
Information: 080-1421-444
Tourist information: 041-52-1315

Directions:

From M4 (Settlers Way), take R102 (Russell St). Turn left into Rink St, and ground is on left, past War Memorial.

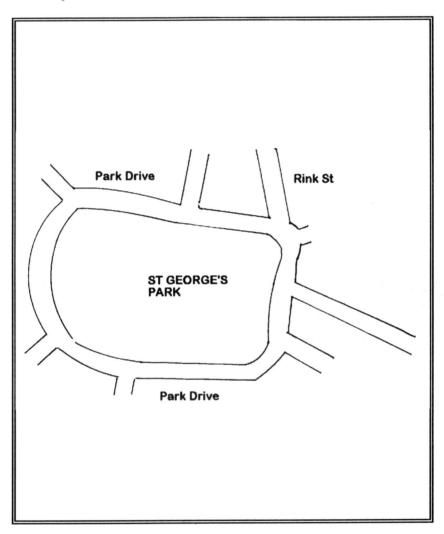

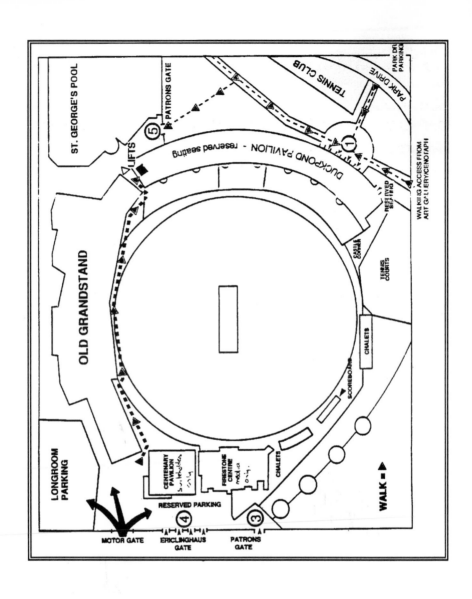

St George's Park Plan - courtesy of Eastern Province Cricket Board

Sri Lanka

Grounds:
Colombo: R. Premadasa (Khettarama) Stadium
Colombo: Sinhalese Sports Club
Kandy: Asgiriya Stadium

Governing Body:
Board of Control for Cricket in Sri Lanka
35, Maitland Place
Colombo 7
Sri Lanka
Tel: 01-434017 or 01-421720
Fax: 01-697405

Tourist information:
22, Regent Street
London SW1
Tel: 0171-930-2627

R.Premadasa (Khettarama) Cricket Stadium

About the ground: First Test match in 1992, against Australia. The ground is in the heart of the commercial centre in Colombo reclaimed from swamp land some ten years ago. The permanent covered stand around the edge of the ground can accommodate some 40,000 spectators

Address: Sri Saddharma Mawatha, Colombo,
Telephone: 01-685780   **Fax:**None
Ticket Office: As above
Capacity: 40,000

Travel:
Nearest station: Maradana   *Tourist information:* 01-437059

Directions:
From the fort area, take D.R. Wijewardena Mawatha. Left by the Maradana station, then right into Sri Saddaharma Mawatha, and ground is on left.

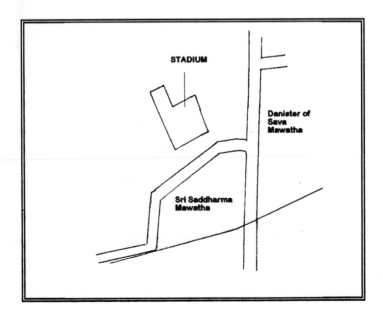

226

Sinhalese Sports Club Cricket Ground

About the ground: The 'Lord's' of Sri Lanka was built on a old aerodrome and came into existence in 1952. The Colombo Cricket Ground, another Test venue is just down the road in a city which has four of them. But the SSC is the show piece with a capacity of 30,000 on great occasions when temporary stands are erected.

Address: Maitland Place, Colombo,
Telephone: 01-695362   **Fax:** None
Ticket Office: As above
Capacity: 30,000

Travel:
Nearest station: Narahenpita or Bambalapitiya (both about 1 mile)

Tourist information: 01-437059

Directions:
The Ground is near Viharamahadevi Park. From Albert Crescent take Indepedence Avenue, turn right into Guildford Crescent and left into Maitland Place. Ground on left.

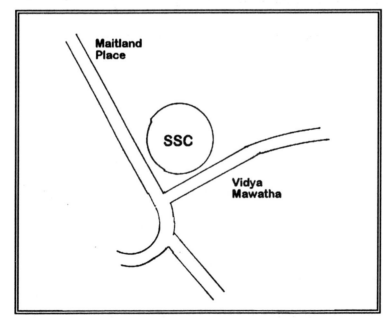

Kandy: Asgiriya Cricket Stadium

About the ground: This ground is accommodated on the playing fields of Trinity College, and was transformed into a Test venue in 1983 replacing the original playing area in a scenic setting with the Knuckles mountains in the background. There are 1,000 fixed seats in the new pavilion, and open cement terraces on half the ground.

Address: Asgiriya Cricket Stadium, Trinity College, Kandy
Telephone: 08-225377   **Fax:** None
Ticket Office: As above
Capacity: 12,000

General facilities:
Cricket souveniers shop: No
Cricket museum: No
Other sporting or recreational *facilities at the ground:* Athletics and hockey. Old Trinitians Sports Club has facilities for members and guests.

Facilities and access for people with disabilities:
Wheelchair access to the ground: No
Good viewing areas inside the ground for people using wheelchairs: No
Toilets for people with disabilities: No

Food & drink:
Full restaurant/dining facilities: No
Fast food facilities: Yes
Tea, coffee, light snacks & biscuits: Yes

Travel:
Car parking: Limited parking near ground. Parking on by pass road from Police station to Mahiyawa.
Nearest station: Kandy
Buses: Walking distance from town centre
Tourist information: 08-222661

Directions:
None received.

Antigua: Recreation Ground, St Johns (RO)

Barbados: Kensington Oval, Bridgetown (RO)

West Indies

Grounds:

Bridgetown, Barbados:	Kensington Oval
Georgetown, Guyana:	Bourda
Kingston, Jamaica:	Sabina Park
Kingstown, St Vincent:	Arnos Vale
Port-of-Spain, Trinidad:	Queen's Park Oval
St John's, Antigua:	Recreation Ground

Governing Body:
The West Indies Cricket Board
PO Box 616 W, Woods Centre
St John's
Antigua
West Indies
Tel: 460-5462-64
Fax: 460-5452/53

Tourist Information:
Antigua and Barbuda Tourist Office: 15 Thayer Street, W1
Tel: 0171-486-7073
Barbados Board of Tourism: 263 Tottenham Court Road, W1
Tel: 0171-636-0090
Guyana High Commission: 3 Palace Court, W2
Tel: 0171-229-7684/8
Jamaica Tourist Board : 1 Prince Consort Road, SW7
Tel: 0171-584-8894
St Vincent & Grenadines Tourist Office: 10,Kensington Crt, W8
Tel: 0171-937-6570
Trinidad & Tobago: 42 Belgrave Square, SW1
Tel: 0171-245-9351

Bridgetown, Barbados: Kensington Oval

About the ground: Test cricket was first played at Kensington Oval in 1930, the first West Indian ground to stage a Test match. The Sir Garfield Sobers Pavilion, The Three W's and Hall and Griffiths stands and the Challenor stand provide good covered seating accommodation and a first class renovation of the ground. The combination of bright colours, drum beat, rapturous applause, palm trees and all the fun of the fair personify joyful Carribean cricket occasions. England won there in April 1994 for the first time in 59 years!

Address: Barbados Cricket Association, Kensington Oval, Fontabelle, St Michael, Bridgetown, Barbados
Postal address: As above
Telephone: 246-436-1397   **Fax:** 246-436-3945
Ticket Office: As above
Ticket information: Contact ticket office
Capacity: 15,000

General facilities:

Cricket souveniers shop: Yes

Cricket museum: No

Other sporting or recreational facilities at the ground: Hockey

Facilities and access for people with disabilities:

Wheelchair access to the ground: Yes
Good viewing areas inside the ground for people using wheelchairs: Yes
Toilets for people with disabilities: No

Food & drink:

Full restaurant/dining facilities: No
Fast food facilities: Yes
Tea, coffee, light snacks & biscuits: Yes
Bars: Yes

Travel:

Car parking: Street and local parking only.

Buses: From city centre terminus.

For Test matches, some hotels arrange transport to the ground.

Tourist information: 246-427-2623/4

Directions: From city centre, take Broad Street towards Cheapside district. This becomes Cheapside, and leads into Fontabelle. Ground on right.

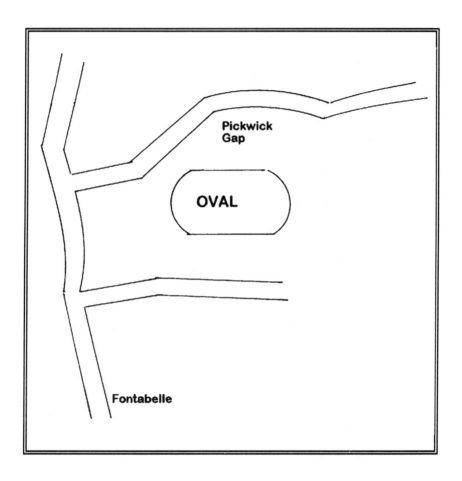

Georgetown, Guyana: Bourda

About the ground: The first Test in Georgetown was in 1929-30 and the occasion of the West Indies first win over England; the great George Headley made a century in both innings. Georgetown is actually built below sea level, buttressed by a long sea wall surrounding weather boarded, stilt raised houses and a combination of frequent rain and a very good pitch have meant that the last conclusive result in any Test match was Hutton's team's success in 1953. Next door to Georgetown Football Club.

Address: Bourda Cricket Ground, Georgetown Cricket Club, New Garden Street, Georgetown, Guyana
Telephone: 02-77130 or 02-54813 (Cricket Board), 02-63404 (Ground)
Fax: None
Ticket Office: Contact Cricket Board as above

Travel:
Tourist information: 02-62505.

Directions:
From St George's Cathedral, North Street, which becomes North Road, leads directly to the Ground.

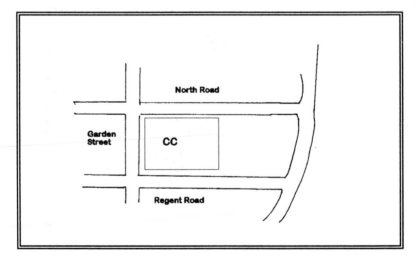

Kingston, Jamaica: Sabina Park

About the ground: This great Test match arena set in the grandeur of the Blue Mountains is small, square and with tall stands and a torrid atmosphere is a cauldron of excitement and cricketing rivalry with spectators close to the players and the pitch.First staged Test cricket in April 1930.

Address: South Camp Road, Kingston, Jamaica
Postal address: Jamaica Cricket Association, George Headley Stand, Sabina Park, Kingston, Jamaica
Telephone: 967-0322   **Fax:** 967-3976
Ticket Office: As above

Travel:
Nearest station: Kingston   *Tourist information:* 929-9200/19

Directions:
Ground is in downtown area of Kingston. From Harbour Street, turn left into South Camp Road and head north. Ground is on left, after junction with North Street.

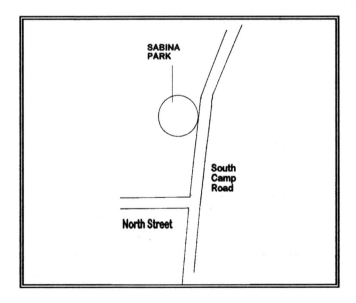

Kingstown, St Vincent: Arnos Vale

About the Ground: Used for one day internationals.

Address: Arnos Vale Playing Field
Postal Address: Windward Islands Cricket Board, PO Box 1493, Kingstown, St Vincent
Telephone: 456-2567   **Fax:** 457-2964
Ticket Office: As above

Directions: Arnos Vale is west of Kingstown. The ground is near the E.T. Joshua Airport.

Tea interval, Antigua (RO)

Port-of-Spain, Trinidad: Queen's Park Oval

About the ground: The Queens Park ground is widely described as unique, framed in the Northern Range mountains in an area of tropical splendid tropical vegetation. The various stands are shaded by enormous, scarlet flowering tulip trees and the ground is adjacent to open parkland in the centre of the city. First staged test cricket in 1930.

Address: Tragarete Road, Port-of- Spain, Trinidad
Postal Address: Trinidad & Tobago Cricket Board, The Cricket Secretariat, Couva Shopping Complex, Isaac Junction, Couva, Trinidad
Telephone: 622-3787 or 622-2295 **Fax:** 622-3787
Ticket Office: 636-1577
Ticket information: Test match tickets available, incluidng five day, first 3 days or last 2 days sets of tickets.
Capacity: 25,000 (19,000 paid, 6,000 other)

General facilities:
Cricket souveniers shop: Yes
Cricket museum: No
Other sporting or recreational facilities at the ground: Yes - football, tennis, squash and hockey.

Facilities and access for people with disabilities:
Wheelchair access to the ground: No
Good viewing areas inside the ground for people using wheelchairs: No
Toilets for people with disabilities: No
Special arrangements made for people with disabilites. Contact ground for details

Food & drink:
Full restaurant/dining facilities: No
Fast food facilities: Yes
Tea, coffee, light snacks & biscuits: Yes
Bars: Yes

Travel:
Car parking: Some at ground - south east corner members only
Buses: From city centre.
Tourist information: 623-1932/4

Directions:

Queen's Park Oval is north west of the city centre. From Park Street, fork right onto Tragarete Road, and ground is on right, at junction with Elizabeth Street.

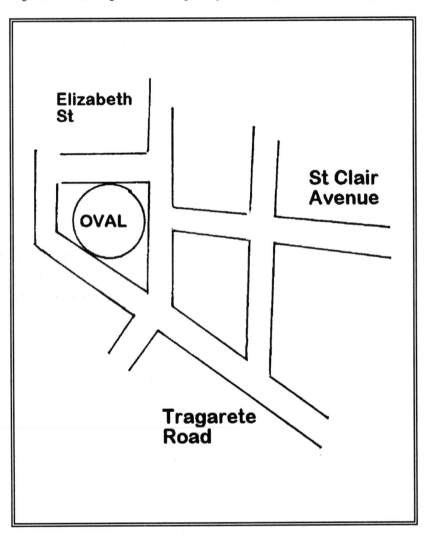

St John's, Antigua: Recreation Ground

About the ground: First used for Test cricket in 1981. The ground where Lara (375) broke Gary Sobers' world record Test score in April 1994. A delightful cricket setting on this tiny island. Seating is a combination of the old and the new; the ancient stand literally shaking with human masses besides the splendid new Viv Richards stand with covered tiers, easy access and circulation. Also visit the Viv Richards Museum on Viv Richards Street.

Address: Independence Avenue, St John's
Postal Address: Leeward Islands Cricket Association, Corner Cross & New Streets, PO Box 1267, St John's, Antigua
Telephone: None available   **Fax:** None

Travel:
Tourist information: 462-0480

Directions:
Independence Avenue is east of the Old Pier. From the harbour, take Long Street east, and turn left. Ground on right. Near Government House and the Catholic Cathedral.

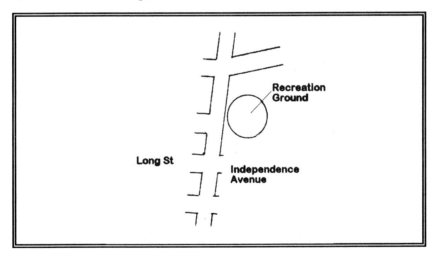

Zimbabwe

Grounds
Bulawayo: Queens Sports Club
Harare: Harare Sports Club

Governing Body:
Zimbabwe Cricket Union
PO Box 2739
Harare
Zimbabwe
Tel: 04-704616/7/8
Fax: 04-729370

Tourist Information:
Zimbabwe Tourist Office
Zimbabwe High Commission
429 Strand
London WC2
Tel: 0171-240-6169
Fax: 0171-240-5465

Bulawayo: Queens Sports Club

About the ground: The original centre for Cricket in Bulawayo, but then lost first class status. First Test matches in city at Athletic Club, but the better facilities at Queens Sports Club has meant matches have returned there. First Test match in 1994 against Sri Lanka.

Address: Corner Robert Mugabe Way and First Avenue
Postal Address: PO Box 868, Bulawayo
Telephone: 09-63642   **Fax:** 09-60130
Ticket Office: Contact club
Ticket information: Test match tickets around Z$200 per match
Capacity: 12,000

General facilities:
Cricket souveniers shop: Yes
Cricket museum: No
Other sporting or recreational facilities at the ground: Squash, hockey, snooker, tennis and basketball.

Facilities and access for people with disabilities:
Wheelchair access to the ground: Yes
Good viewing areas inside the ground for people using wheelchairs: Yes - open grandstands
Toilets for people with disabilities: No

Food & drink:
Full restaurant/dining facilities: No
Fast food facilities: Yes . Includes braais (barbacues) and biltong
Tea, coffee, light snacks & biscuits: Yes
Bars: Yes

Travel:
Car parking: Members only at ground. Non members local parking within 100 yards
Nearest station: Bulawayo (1.5 miles)
Buses: None to ground. Stop about 4 blocks away. Taxis from city centre.
Tourist information: 09-74055

241

Directions:

From city centre, go north on Robert Mugabe Way, and ground is on left, at corner of First Avenue.

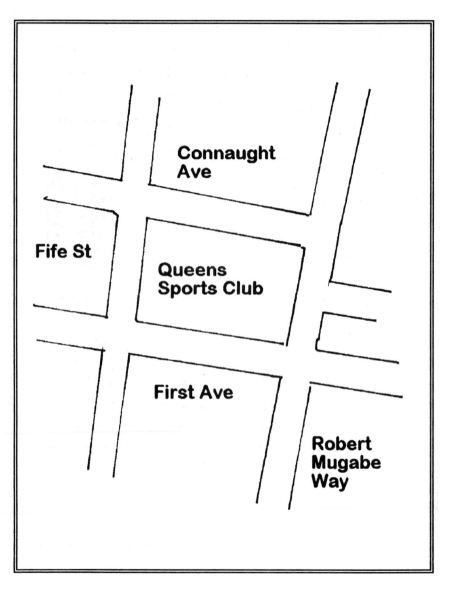

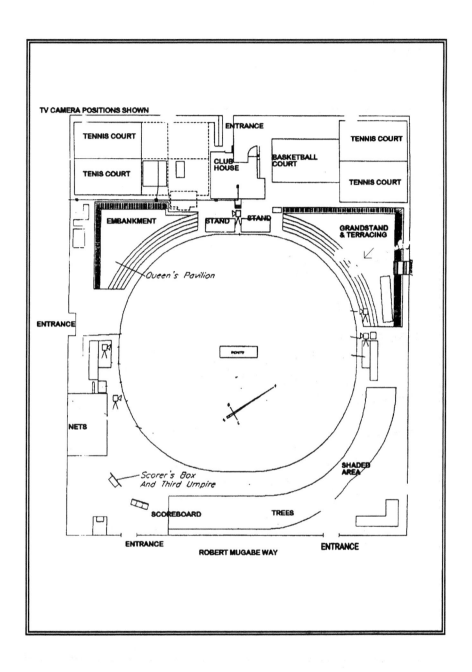

Plan of Queens Sports Club - courtesy of Queens Sports Club

Harare: Harare Sports Club

About the Ground: First ground in Zimbabwe to stage a Test match, against India in 1992

Address: Corner Josiah Tongogara Avenue and Fifth Street
Postal Address: PO Box 1104, Harare
Telephone: 04-791151   **Fax:** None
Ticket Office: As above
Ticket information: Tickets from central sales point. Test matches Z$40, one day internationals Z$80
Capacity: 10,000 (approx)

General facilities:
Cricket souveniers shop: Yes

Cricket museum: No

Other sporting or recreational facilities at the ground: Rugby Union

Facilities and access for people with disabilities:
Wheelchair access to the ground: Yes
Good viewing areas inside the ground for people using wheelchairs: Yes
Toilets for people with disabilities: Yes

Food & drink:
Full restaurant/dining facilities: Yes - meals available
Fast food facilities: Yes
Tea, coffee, light snacks & biscuits: Yes
Bars: Yes

Travel:
Car parking: Members only at ground.
Local parking
Nearest station: Harare (1.5 miles)

Buses: Taxis from city centre
Tourist information: 04-752570

Directions:

From city centre take Second Avenue north. Turn right into Josiah Tongogara Avenue, and ground is on left at corner of Fifth Street

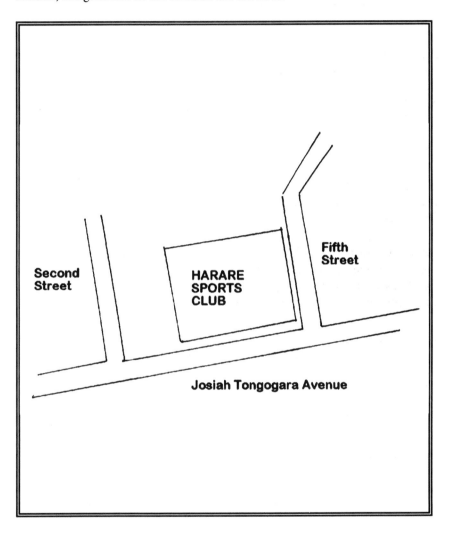

Rugby League Books

The Sin Bin

A new collection of Rugby League cartoons and humour. Caricatures of leading people in the game ... the Adventures of Mo ... The Flatcappers... Bath v Wigan ... Life Down South ... and much more.

Price: £5.95. Published in October 1996.

I Wouldn't Start from Here
A Travelling Supporters' Guide to British Rugby League grounds

Includes details of ground facilities, price discounts, road directions and public transport information. Sponsored by the Rugby League Supporters Association. Published in April 1996. Includes over 30 photos. **Excellent value at £5.00.** Includes free 1997 supplement

Touch and Go
A History of Professional Rugby League in London

From the clubs in the 1930s to the London Broncos. Includes all the international matches played in London, and the first Wembley Cup Final. Interviews with key people involved in Fulham, London Crusaders and the Broncos. Many photos and illustrations, and comprehensive statistics. **Published August 1995. 380 pages for just £9.00.**

To order any of the above books, make cheques payable to: London League Publications Ltd, and send to: London League Publications Ltd, PO Box 10441, London E14 0SB. Special offers for readers of this book: All books post free. Order all three books for only £18.00

1997 Cricket Fixtures

We would like to thank the England and Wales Cricket Board and Minor Counties Cricket Association for permission to use the First Class and Minor Counties fixtures. The fixtures are correct at the time of production - check in the press or with the County if in doubt. We apologise for not including all Minor Counties fixtures - space restrictions precluded this.

(s): Includes Sunday play

April

Tue 15
Fenner's: Cambridge U v Derbyshire
The Parks: Oxford U v Durham

Wed 16
Headingley : Yorkshire v Lancashire (4 days)

Fri 18   *Tetley's Shield*
Edgbaston: 'England 'A' v The Rest (s)
(4 days)
Other Matches
Fenner's: Cambridge Univ v Leicesters're
The Parks: Oxford Univ v Hampshire

Wed 23
Britannic Assurance Championship
Chelmsford: Essex v Hampshire
Cardiff: Glamorgan v Warwickshire
Canterbury: Kent v Derbyshire
Old Trafford: Lancashire v Durham
Leicester: Leices v Gloucestershire
Trent Bridge:Notts v Worcestershire
The Foster's Oval: Surrey v Somerset
Hove: Sussex v Northamptonshire
Other Matches
Fenner's: Cambridge Univ v Middlesex
The Parks: Oxford Univ v Yorkshire

Sat 26
The Parks: British Univ v Yorkshire
(1 day)

Sun 27   *AXA Life League*
Chelmsford: Essex v Hampshire
Cardiff: Glamorgan vWarwickshire
Canterbury : Kent v Derbyshire
Old Trafford: Lancashire v Durham
Leicester: Leices v Gloucestershire
Trent Bridge: Notts v Worcestershire
The Foster's Oval: Surrey v Somerset
Hove: Sussex v Northamptonshire

Mon 28   *Benson and Hedges Cup*
Chelmsford: Essex v Glamorgan
Bristol: Gloucestershire v British Univ
Dublin (Clontarf): Ireland v Middlesex
Old Trafford: Lancashire v Yorkshire
Leicester: Leicestershire v Scotland
Lakenham: Minor C v Derbyshire
Trent Bridge: Nottis v Durham
The Foster's Oval: Surrey v Kent
Hove: Sussex v Hampshire
Worcester: Worcest v Warwickshire

Wed 30   *Benson and Hedges Cup*
Fenner's: British Universities v Sussex
Chester-le-Street: Durham v Northants
Bristol: Gloucestershire v Surrey
Canterbury : Kent v Hampshire
Old Trafford: Lancashire v Derbyshire
Leicester: Leices v Nottinghamshire
Lord's: Middlesex v Essex
Taunton: Somerset v Glamorgan
Edgbaston: Warwickshire v Minor C
Headingley: Yorkshire v Worces

May

Fri 2   *Benson and Hedges Cup*
Derby: Derbyshire v Yorkshire
Cardiff: Glamorgan v Middlesex
Southampton: Hants v Gloucestershire
Canterbury : Kent v Sussex
Trent Bridge:Notts v Northamptonshire
Forfar: Scotland v Durham
Taunton: Somerset v Ireland
The Foster's Oval: Surrey v Brit Univ
Edgbaston:Warwickshire v Lancashire
Worcester: Worcestershire v Minor C

Sun 4   *AXA Life League*
Derby : Derbyshire v Lancashire
Chelmsford: Essex v Middlesex
Southampton: Hampshire v Yorkshire
Canterbury: Kent v Surrey
Taunton: Somerset v Glamorgan
Hove: Sussex v Nottinghamshire
Edgbaston: Warwicks v Northants

Mon 5   *Benson and Hedges Cup*
Derby: Derbyshire v Worcestershire
Chester-le-Street:Durham v Leices
Chelmsford: Essex v Somerset
Cardiff: Glamorgan v Ireland
Southampton: Hampshire v Surrey
Canterbury: Kent v British Universities
Walsall: Minor Counties v Lancashire
Northampton: Northants v Scotland
Hove: Sussex v Gloucestershire
Edgbaston: Warwickshire v Yorkshire

Wed 7
Britannic Assurance Championship
Derby: Derbyshire v Surrey
Hartlepool: Durham v Nottinghamshire
Bristol: Gloucestershire v Hampshire
Lord's: Middlesex v Sussex
Northampton: Northants v Somerset
Worcester: Worces v Leicestershire
Headingley: Yorkshire v Glamorgan
Other Matches
Fenner's: Cambridge U v Essex
The Parks: Oxford U v Warwickshire

Sun 11   *AXA Life League*
Derby: Derbyshire v Surrey
Hartlepool: Durham v Nottinghamshire
Bristol: Gloucestershire v Hampshire
Lord's: Middlesex v Sussex
Northampton: Northants v Somerset
Worcester: Worces v Leicestershire
Headingley: Yorkshire v Glamorgan

Mon 12   *Benson and Hedges Cup*
The Parks: British Univ v Hampshire
Derby: Derbyshire v Warwickshire
Bristol: Gloucestershire v Kent
Downpatrick: Ireland v Essex
Old Trafford:Lancs v Worcestershire
Lord's: Middlesex v Somerset
Northampton:Northants v Leics
Glasgow(Titwood):Scotland v Notts
The Foster's Oval: Surrey v Sussex
Headingley : Yorkshire v Minor C

Wed 14
Bntannic Assurance Championship
Chelmsford: Essex v Durham
Southampton: Hants v Leicestershire
Canterbury : Kent v Glamorgan
Old Trafford: Lancs v Nottinghamshire
Lord's: Middlesex v Derbyshire
Taunton: Somerset v Sussex
The Foster's Oval: Surrey v Gloucs
Edgbaston: Warwicktshire v Yorkshire
Other Matches
Fenner's: Cambridge U v Northants
The Parks: Oxford U v Worcestershire

Thu 15   *Tourist Match* (1 day)
Arundel: Duke of Norfolk's XI v Australia

Sat 17   *Tourist Match* (1 day)
Northampton: Northamptonshire v Australia
Other Match
Fenner's:Cambridge Univ v Oxford Univ (1 day)

Sun 18   *AXA Life League*
Chelmsford: Essex v Durham
Southampton: Hants v Leicestershire
Canterbury: Kent v Glamorgan
Old Trafford: Lancs v Nottinghamshire
Lord's: Middlesex v Derbyshire
Taunton: Somerset v Sussex
The Foster's Oval: Surrey v Gloucs
Edgbaston: Warwickshire v Yorkshire
Tourist Match
Worcester: Worcestershire v Australia (1 day)
Minor Counties: MCC Trophy Preliminary
Round

Mon 19 *Bain Hogg Insurance Trophy*
Leek: Minor Counties v Warwickshire II
Tue 20   *Tourist Match*
Chester-le-Street Durham v Australia (1 day)
Bain Hogg Insurance Trophy
Leek: Minor Counties v Leicestershire II

Wed 21
Britannic Assurance Championship
Chester-le-Street: Durham v Worcs
Cardiff: Glamorgan v Hampshire
Gloucester: Gloucestershire v Essex
Old Trafford: Lancs v Northants
Leicester: Leicestershire v Surrey
Trent Bridge: Notts v Derbyshire
Taunton: Somerset v Yorkshire
Horsham: Sussex v Kent
Edgbaston: Warwickshire v Middlesex

248

Thu 22   *Texaco Trophy*
Headingley: (1st 1-Day International)
ENGLAND v AUSTRALIA
(Reserve day Friday 23 May)

Sat 24   *Texaco Trophy*
The Foster's Oval:
(2nd 1-Day International)
ENGLAND v AUSTRALIA

Sun 25   *Texaco Trophy*
Lord's: (3rd 1-Day International)
 ENGLAND v AUSTRALIA
 (Reserve day Mon 26 May)
AXA Life League
Chester-le-Street: Durham v Worcs
Cardiff: Glamorgan v Hampshire
Gloucester: Gloucestershire v Essex
Old Trafford: Lancs v Northants
Leicester: Leicestershire v Surrey
Trent Bridge: Notts v Derbyshire
Taunton: Somerset v Yorkshire
Horsham: Sussex v Kent
Edgbaston: Warwickshire v Middlesex

Tue 27   *Benson and Hedges Cup*
Quarter Finals
Tetley's Challenge Series
Bristol or Hove:
Gloucestershire or Sussex v Australia
(or Surrey v Australia at The Foster's Oval if
both in B & H matches)

Thu 29
Britannic Assurance Championship
Ilford: Essex v Yorkshire
Cardiff: Glamorgan v Durham
Southampton: Hants v Warwickshire
Leicester: Leicestershire v Lancashire
Lord's: Middlesex v Northamptonshire
Trent Bridge: Nottinghamshire v Kent
Worcester: Worcestershire v Somerset

Fri 30
The Parks: Oxford U v Sussex

Sat 31   *Tetley's Challenge Series*
Derby: Derbyshire v Australia (s)

June

Sun 1   *AXA Life League*
Ilford: Essex v Yorkshire

Pontypridd: Glamorgan v Durham
Southampton: Hants v Walwickshire
Leicester: Leicestershire v Lancashire
Lord's: Middlesex v Northamptonshire
Trent Bridge: Nottinghamshire v Kent
Worcester: Worcestershire v Somerset
Minor Counties:
MCC Trophy 1st Round

Mon 2 *Bain Hogg Insurance Trophy*
N.Runcton: Minor C v Northants II

Tue 3 *Bain Hogg Insurance Trophy*
Melton Mowbray: Leics II v Minor C

Wed 4
Britannic Assurance Championship
Chesterfield: Derbyshire v Hampshire
Chester-le-Street: Durham v Sussex
Tunbridge Wells: Kent v Warwicks
Lord's: Middlesex v Leicestershire
Northampton: Northants v Notts
Taunton: Somerset v Lancashire
The Foster's Oval: Surrey v Essex
Headingley: Yorkshire v Gloucs

Thu 5
Cornhill Insurance Test Match
Edgbaston: (First Test Match)
ENGLAND v AUSTRALIA (s)
Other Match
The Parks: Oxford U v Glamorgan

Sun 8   *AXA Life League*
Chesterfield: Derbyshire v Hampshire
Chester-le-Street: Durham v Sussex
Tunbridge Wells: Kent v Warwickshire
Lord's: Middlesex v Leicestershire
Milton Keynes: Northants v Notts
Taunton: Somerset v Lancashire
The Foster's Oval: Surrey v Essex
Headingley: Yorkshire v Gloucs

Mon 9   *Costcutter Cup*
Harrogate   (Three days)

Tue 10   *Benson and Hedges Cup*
Semi Finals (Reserve day 11 June)
Bain Hogg Insurance Trophy
Sleaford: Minor C V Middlesex II

Wed 11   *Tetley's Challenge Series*
Northampton or Trent Bridge:
Northamptonshire or Notts v Australia

(If both in B & H semi finals, Durham to play Australia)

Thur 12
Britannic Assurance Championship
Cardiff: Glamorgan v Middlesex
Bristol: Gloucs v Worcestershire
Basingstoke: Hampshire v Somerset
Old Trafford: Lancashire v Kent
The Foster's Oval: Surrey vYorkshire
Hove: Sussex v Essex
Edgbaston: Warwickshire v Derbyshire

Sat 14 *Tetley's Challenge Senes*
Leicester: Leicestershire v Australia (s)
Other Matches
Fenner's: Cambridge U v Durham (s)
The Parks: Oxford U v Notts

Sun 15 *AXA Life League*
Cardiff: Glamorgan v Middlesex
Bristol: Gloucs v Worcestershire
Basingstoke: Hampshire v Somerset
Old Trafford: Lancashire v Kent
The Foster's Oval: Surrey vYorkshire
Hove: Sussex v Essex
Edgbaston: Warwickshire v Derbyshire

Wed 18
Britannic Assurance Championship
Derby: Derbyshire v Sussex
Darlington: Durham v Kent
Bristol: Gloucestershire v Middlesex
Liverpool: Lancashire v Glamcrgan
Northampton: Northants v Hampshire
Trent Bridge: Notts vYorkshire
Bath: Somerset v Leicestershire
Worcester: Worcestershire v Surrey

Thu 19
Cornhill Insurance Test Match
Lord's: (Second Test Match)
ENGLAND v AUSTRALIA (s)

Fri 20
Chelmsford: Essex v Oxford Univ (s)

Sun 22 *AXA Life League*
Derby: Derbyshire v Sussex
Darlington: Durham v Kent
Bristol: Gloucestershire v Middlesex
Old Trafford: Lancashire v Glamorgan
Northampton: Northants v Hampshire

Trent Bridge: Notts v Yorkshire
Bath: Somerset v Leicestershire
Worcester: Worcestershire v Surrey
Minor Counties:
MCC Trophy Quarter Finals

Tue 24
NatWest Trophy First Round
Beaconsfield: Bucks v Essex
Wisbech: Cambridgeshire v Hampshire
Barrow: Cumberland v Northants
Exmouth: Devon v Leicestershire
Cardiff: Glamorgan v Bedfordshire
Bristol: Gloucestershire v Scotland
Old Trafford: Lancashire v Berkshire
Lincoln Lindum: Lincs v Derbyshire
Lord's: Middlesex v Kent
Trent Bridge: Notts v Staffordshire
Taunton: Somerset v Herefordshire
The Foster's Oval: Surrey v Durham
Hove: Sussex v Shropshire
Edgbaston: Warwickshire v Norfolk
Worcester: Worcestershire v Holland
Headingley: Yorkshire v Ireland

Wed 25 *Tourist Match*
The Parks: British Univ v Australia

Thu 26
Britannic Assurance Championship
Southend: Essex v Derbyshire
Swansea: Glamorgan v Sussex
Leicester: Leics v Warwickshire
Luton: Northants v Gloucestershire
The Foster's Oval: Surrey v Notts
Worcester: Worcs v Lancashire
Headingley: Yorkshire v Middlesex

Sat 28 *Tetley's Challenge Series*
Southampton: Hants v Australia (s)
Other Matches
Canterbury: Kent v Cambridge U (s)
Taunton: Somerset v Oxford U (s)

Sun 29 *AXA Life League*
Southend: Essex v Derbyshire
Swansea: Glamorgan v Sussex
Leicester:Leics v Warwickshire
Luton:Northants v Gloucestershire
The Foster's Oval: Surrey v Notts
Worcester: Worcs v Lancashire
Headingley: Yorkshire v Middlesex

July

Wed 2:

Britannic Assurance Championship
Chester-le-Street: Durham v Hants
Chelmsford: Essex v Somerset
Swansea: Glamorgan v Gloucestershire
Maidstone: Kent v Northamptonshire
Leicester: Leicestershire v Yorkshire
Uxbridge: Middlesex v Lancashire
Arundel: Sussex v Worcestershire
Edgbaston: Warwickshire v Surrey
Tourist Match (3 days)
Trent Bridge: Notts v Pakistan 'A'
Varsity Match (3 days)
Lord's: Oxford Uv Cambridge U

Thur 3
Cornhill Insurance Test Match
Old Trafford: (3rd Test Match)
ENGLAND v AUSTRALIA (s)

Sat 5   *Tourist Match* (3 days)
Derby :Derbyshire v Pakistan 'A'

Sun 6   *AXA Life League*
Chester-le-Street: Durham v Hants
Chelmsford: Essex v Somerset
Swansea: Glamorgan v Gloucestershire
Maidstone: Kent v Northamptonshire
Leicester: Leicestershire v Yorkshire
Uxbridge: Middlesex v Lancashire
Arundel: Sussex v Worcestershire
Edgbaston: Warwickshire v Surrey

Wed 9 *NatWest Trophy 2nd Round*
Marlow or Chelmsford: Bucks or Essex v
Worcestershire or Holland
Wisbech or Southampton:
Cambridgeshire or Hampshire v
Glamorgan or Bedfordshire
Exmouth or Leicester: Devon or Leicestershire
v Yorkshire or Ireland
Lincoln Lindum or Derby:
Lincolnshire or Derbyshire v
Cumberland or Northamptonshire
Uxbridge or Canterbury:
Middlesex or Kent v
Gloucestershire or Scotland
The Foster's Oval or Chester-le-Street:
Surrey or Durham v Nottinghamshire or
Staffordshire
Hove or St Georges(Telford)
Sussex or Shropshire v Lancashire or Berkshire

Edgbaston or Lakenham
Warwickshire or Norfolk v Somerset or
Herefordshire

Tourist Matches
Jesmond: Minor C v Australia (1 day)
Shenley: MCC v Pakistan 'A': (3 days)

Thu 10 *Bain Hogg Insurance Trophy*
W.Bromwich: Warwickshire II v Minor C

Sat 12
Lord's: *Benson and Hedges Cup Final*
(Reserve days 13 & 14 July)
Tourist Match: (1 day)
Edinburgh: (Grange CC) Scotland v Australia
Other Match: (1 day)
Scarborough: Yorkshire v Durham
(Northern Electric Trophy)

Sun 13   *AXA Life League*
Derby: Derbyshire v Yorkshire
Chester-le-Street:Durham v Warwicks
Southampton: Hampshire v Worcs
Trent Bridge: Notts v Somerset
Hove: Sussex v Gloucestershire
(Matches for B&H Cup finalists to be played on
Tuesday 15 July)
Tourist Match (1 day)
Walsall: ECB XI v Pakistan 'A'
McCain Challenge (1 day)
Scarborough: Surrey v Leicestershire

Mon 14 *Tetley Bitter Festival Trophy* (1 day)
Scarborough: Yorkshire v The Yorkshiremen

Wed 16
Britannic Assurance Championship
Cheltenham: Gloucs v Derbyshire
Canterbury : Kent v Leicestershire
Old Trafford: Lancashire v Sussex
Northampton: Northants v Essex
Trent Bridge: Notts v Warwickshire
Guildford: Surrey v Hampshire
Scarborough: Yorkshire v Durham
Tetley's Challenge Senes
Cardiff: Glamorgan v Australia

Tourist Match: (3 days)
Worcester: Worcs v Pakistan 'A'

Sat 19
Tetley's Challenge Series
Lord's: Middlesex v Australia (s)

Tourist Match (3 days)
Taunton: Somerset v Pakistan 'A'

Sun 20   *AXA Life League*
Cheltenham: Gloucs v Derbyshire
Canterbury: Kent v Leicestershire
Old Trafford: Lancashire v Sussex
Northampton: Northants v Essex
Trent Bridge: Notts v Warwickshire
Guildford: Surrey v Hampshire
Worcester: Worcs v Glamorgan
Scarborough: Yorkshire v Durham
Minor Counties:
MCC Trophy Semi Finals

Mon 21 *Bain Hogg Insurance Trophy*
Milton Keynes: Northants II v Minor C

Tue 22   *Tourist Match* (1 day)
Cheltenham: Gloucs v Pakistan 'A'
Bain Hogg Insurance Trophy
Uxbridge: Middlesex II v Minor C

Wed 23
Britannic Assurance Championship
Chesterfield: Derbyshire v Glamorgan
Chelmsford: Essex v Worcestershire
Cheltenham: Gloucestershire v Durham
Southampton: Hampshire v Lancashire
Leicester: Leicestershire v Notts
Lord's: Middlesex v Kent
Northampton: Northants v Surrey
Edgbaston: Warwickshire v Somerset

Thu 24
Cornhill Insurance Test Match
Headingley   (4th Test Match)
ENGLAND v AUSTRALIA (s)

Tourist Match (4 days)
Hove: Sussex v Pakistan 'A' (s)

Sun 27   *AXA Life League*
Chesterfield: Derbyshire v Glamorgan
Chelmsford: Essex v Worcestershire
Cheltenham: Gloucestershire v Durham
Southampton: Hampshire v Lancashire
Leicester: Leics v Nottinghamshire
Lord's: Middlesex v Kent
Northampton: Northants v Surrey
Edgbaston: Warwickshire v Somerset

Tue 29
NatWest Trophy Quarter Finals
Tourist Match   (1 day)
Cardiff or Southampton:
Glamorgan or Hampshire v Pakistan 'A'
(Depends on results in NWT round 2)

Thu 31
Britannic Assurance Championship
Chester-le-Street: Durham v Derbys
Colchester: Essex v Leicestershire
Colwyn Bay: Glamorgan v Notts
Edgbaston: Warwickshire v Sussex
Worcester: Worcestershire v Kent
Headingley: Yorkshire v Northants
Tourist Match (1 day)
Swansea: Wales v Pakistan 'A'

August

Fri 1
Tetley's Challenge Senes (4 days)
Taunton: Somerset v Australia (s)
Tounst Match (4 days)
Bristol: Gloucestershire v Pakistan 'A'
NatWest U-19 International Match
Hove: England v Zimbabwe
(1st 1-Day International)

Sun 3   *AXA Life League*
Chester-le-Street: Durham v Derbys
Colchester: Essex v Leicestershire
Colwyn Bay: Glamorgan v Notts
Lord's: Middlesex v Surrey
Edgbaston: Warwickshire v Sussex
Worcester: Worcestershire v Kent
Headingley: Yorkshire v Northants

Mon 4
NatWest U-19 International Match
Southampton: England v Zimbabwe
(2nd 1-Day International)

Wed 6
Bnitannic Assurance Championship
Canterbury: Kent v Essex
Blackpool: Lancashire v Warwickshire
Lord's: Middlesex v Hampshire
Northampton:Northants v Worcs
Taunton: Somerset v Gloucestershire
The Foster's Oval: Surrey v Durham
Eastbourne: Sussex v Leicestershire

Thu 7
Cornhill Insurance Test Match
Trent Bridge (5th Test Match)
ENGLAND v AUSTRALIA (s)
Tourist Match (4 days) (s)
Headingley: Yorkshire v Pakistan 'A'
NatWest Under 19 International Match
Edgbaston:England v Zimbabwe (s)
(1st Test Match) (4 days)

Sat 9   (3 days)
Dublin (Malahide): Ireland v Scotland (s)

Sun 10   *AXA Life League*
Canterbury : Kent v Essex
Old Trafford: Lancs v Warwickshire
Lord's: Middlesex v Hampshire
Northampton: Northants v Worcs
Taunton: Somerset v Gloucestershire
The Foster's Oval: Surrey v Durham
Eastbourne: Sussex v Leicestershire

Tue 12 and Wed 13
NatWest Trophy Semi Finals
Reserve Days for Ist Semi-Final Wed 13 and Thu
14. Reserve Day for 2nd Semi-Final Thu 14.

Tue 12   *Tourist Match*
Derby or Northampton: Derbyshire or
Northamptonshire v Pakistan 'A' (1 day)
Depending on outcome of NWT Second Round

Fri 15
Britannic Assurance Championship
Derby: Derbyshire v Lancashire (s)
Portsmouth: Hampshire v Yorkshire (s)
Lord's: Middlesex v Surrey (s)
Trent Bridge: Notts v Somerset (s)
Hove: Sussex v Gloucestershire (s)
Worcester: Worcs v Glamorgan
Tourist Match
Chelmsford:First Class Counties Select XI v
Pakistan 'A' (4 days) (s)
Women's Cricket International Match
Bristol: England v South Africa
(1st 1 Day International)

Sat 16
Tetley's Challenge Series
Canterbury: Kent v Australia (s)

Sun 17
Women's Cricket International Match
Taunton: England v South Africa

(2nd 1 Day International)

Mon 18 or Tue 19
Bain Hogg Insurance Trophy Semi Finals

Wed 20
Britannic Assurance Championship
Chester-le-Street: Durham v Middlesex
Abergavenny: Glamorgan v Northants
Leicester: Leicestershire v Derbyshire
Worksop: Nottinghamshire v Essex
Taunton: Somerset v Kent
Edgbaston: Warwickshire v Worcs
Scarborough: Yorkshire v Sussex
Women's Cricket International Match
Lord's: England v South Africa
(3rd 1 Day International)

Thu 21
Cornhill Insurance Test Match
The Foster's Oval (6th Test Match)
ENGLANDVAUSTRALIA (s)
NatWest U-19 International Match
Northampton:England v Zimbabwe (s)
(2nd Test Match) (4 days)

Sun 24   *AXA Life League*
Chester-le-Street: Durham v Middlesex
Cardiff: Glamorgan v Northants
Bristol: Gloucestershire v Lancashire
Leicester: Leicestershire v Derbyshire
Trent Bridge: Nottinghamshire v Essex
Taunton: Somerset v Kent
Worcester: Worcs v Warwickshire
Scarborough: Yorkshire v Sussex

Wed 27
Britannic Assurance Championship
Derby : Derbyshire v Somerset
Chelmsford: Essex v Warwickshire
Bristol: Gloucestershire v Notts
Portsmouth: Hampshire v Kent
Old Trafford: Lancashire v Yorkshire
Leicester: Leicestershire v Glamorgan
Northampton: Northants v Durham
Hove: Sussex v Surrey
Kidderminster: Worcs v Middlesex
Women's Cricket International Match
Hinckley : England v South Africa
(4th 1 Day International)

Minor Counties:
Lords: *MCC Trophy Final*

253

Thu 28
NatWest U-19 International Match
Canterbury :England v Zimbabwe (s)
(3rd Test Match) (4 days)

Sat 30
Women's Cricket International Match
Milton Keynes: England v South Africa
(5th 1 Day International)

Sun 31   *AXA Life League*
Derby : Derbyshire v Somerset
Chelmsford: Essex v Warwickshire
Bristol: Gloucestershire v Notts
Portsmouth: Hampshire v Kent
Old Trafford: Lancashire v Yorkshire
Leicester: Leicestershire v Glamorgan
Northampton: Northants v Durham
Hove: Sussex v Surrey
Worcester: Worcs v Middlesex

September

Tue 2
Britannic Assurance Championship
Derby: Derbyshire v Northamptonshire
Chester-le-Street: Durham v Warwicks
Canterbury : Kent v Gloucestershire
Old Trafford: Lancashire v Essex
Trent Bridge: Notts v Hampshire
Taunton: Somerset v Middlesex
The Foster's Oval: Surrey v Glamorgan
Headingley: Yorkshire v Worcs

Sat 6
Lord's: *NATWEST TROPHY FINAL*
Reserve days Sun 7 and Mon 8

Sun 7   *AXA Life League*
Derby: Derbyshire v Northamptonshire
Canterbury : Kent v Gloucestershire
Old Trafford: Lancashire v Essex
Leicester: Leicestershire v Durham
Trent Bridge: Notts v Hampshire
Taunton: Somerset v Middlesex
The Foster's Oval: Surrey v Glamorgan

Headingley: Yorkshire v Worcs
(Matches involving NWT Finalists to be played
on Tue 9)

Mon 8
Bain Hogg Insurance Trophy Final
(venue to be arranged)

Wed 10
Britannic Assurance Championship
Chester-le-Street: Durham v Somerset
Cardiff: Glamorgan v Essex
Southampton: Hampshire v Sussex
Lord's: Middlesex v Nottinghamshire
Northampton: Northants v Leics
The Foster's Oval: Surrey v Lancashire
Edgbaston: Warwickshire v Gloucs
Worcester: Worcs v Derbyshire
Headingley: Yorkshire v Kent

Sun 14   *AXA Life League*
Chester-le-Street: Durham v Somerset
Cardiff: Glamorgan v Essex
Southampton: Hampshire v Sussex
Lord's: Middlesex v Nottinghamshire
Northampton: Northants v Leics
The Foster's Oval: Surrey v Lancashire
Edgbaston: Warwickshire v Gloucs
Worcester: Worcs v Derbyshire
Headingley : Yorkshire v Kent
Minor Counties Championship Final
Venue to be arranged (2 days)

Thu 18
Britannic Assurance Championship
Derby : Derbyshire v Yorkshire (s)
Chelmsford: Essex v Middlesex (s)
Bristol: Gloucestershire v Lancs (s)
Southampton: Hampshire v Worcs (s)
Canterbury : Kent v Surrey (s)
Leicester: Leicestershire v Durham (s)
Taunton: Somerset v Glamorgan (s)
Hove: Sussex v Nottinghamshire (s)
Edgbaston: Warwicks v Northants (s)